ward·ALMOND, Darren·ARNATT, Keith·ARNOLD, Liz·ARROV
Fiona·BARBIERI, Olivo·BARCLAY, Claire·BASEMAN, Jordan
d·BENDON, Helen·BERGER, Adri·BERNARD, Bruce·BEVAN,
nce·BONVIN, Susan·BORLAND, Christine·BOSHIER, Dere
RISLEY, Stuart·BROWN, Don·BROWN, Glenn·BROWN, Jemima·BROWN, Phil
UTLER, Christine·CALLE, Sophie·CALLERY, Simon·CAMPBELL, Steven·CANNON,
AWKWELL, Sarah·CHADWICK, Helen·CHADWICK, Lynn·CHAMBERS, Stephen
ODZKO, Adam·CHUBB, Shirley·CHUHAN, Jagjit·CLOUGH, Prunella·COBB, John
, Joshua·CONNEARN, David·CONSTABLE, Martin·COOK, Ben·COOK, Richard
COPLANS, John·COUTTS, Marion·COVENTRY, Keith·CRAIG-MARTIN, Michael
uan·CUDDIHY, Mikey·CURRALL, Alan·DADE, Adam·DAHN, Walter·DALZIEL,
eter·DAVIES, Tim·DAVIS, Peter·DAWSON, Ian·DAYAN, Eddie·DE MONCHAUX,
eremy·DENIS, Dominic·DENNIS, Jeffrey·DERGES, Susan·DI STEFANO, Arturo
VEN, Anne Katrine·DONNELLY, Micky·DORON, Itai·DOWER, Natalie·DOWSON,
ELLIS, Peter·EMIN, Tracey·ENGLISH, Simon·EVANS, Rachel·FAGEN, Graham
ephen·FEENEY, Jacinta·FEND, Peter·FESENMAIER, Helene·FINN-KELCEY, Rose
FLEURY, Sylvie·FLOYER, Ceal·FORD, Laura·FORSTER, Noel·FORSTER, Peter
atharina·FROST, Judith·FROST, Terry·FRYDLENDER, Barry·FULTON, Hamish
·GENERAL IDEA·GEORGE, Patrick·GHOSH, Amal·GILL, Alison·GILLICK, Liam
WIN, Dryden·GORDON, Douglas·GORMLEY, Antony·GRAHAM, Dan·GRAHAM,
REENWOOD, John·GREGORY, Joy·GRIERSON, Robin Lewis·GRIFFITHS, Brian
HAMILTON, Richard·HANNEY, Sonya·HAPASKA, Siobhán·HARDING, Alexis
hristine·HAYS, Dan·HEAD, Tim·HEATH, Claude·HEMSWORTH, Gerard·HENOCQ,
amien·HOLZER, Jenny·HOOKER, Charlie·HOPKINS, Louise·HOSKING, Mark
Stephen·HUGONIN, James·HUME, Gary·HUSSAIN, Kabir·IMPEY, Sax·INNES,
N, Derek·JOFFE, Chantal·JOHNSON, Glenys·JOHNSON, Nerys·JOHNSON, Steve
Isaac·KABAKOV, Ilya·KAPOOR, Anish·KARSHAN, Linda·KAUR, Permindar·KAY,

Arts Council Collection Acquisitions 1989–2002

Arts Council Collection Acquisitions 1989–2002

An illustrated catalogue of sculpture, painting, drawing, photography, video and installation, artists' prints and multiples acquired for the Arts Council of England between 1989 and 2002

Arts Council Collection Acquisitions 1989–2002

Catalogue designed by Hoop Design
Production coordinated by Uwe Kraus GmbH
Printed in Italy

Published by Hayward Gallery Publishing, London SE1 8XX, UK
© Hayward Gallery 2003
Artworks © the artists or estates of the artists 2003 (unless stated otherwise)
Photographs © Anthony Reynolds Gallery, Anthony Wilkinson Gallery,
Edward Woodman, Frith Street Gallery, Gagosian Gallery, Graham Matthews,
Greengrassi Gallery, Hugo Glendinning, John Riddy, John Searle, John Webb,
Lisson Gallery, Marcus Leith, Martin Roberts, Matt's Gallery, Michael Pollard,
Mike Fear, Mimmo Capone, Robert McKeever, Salvatore Ala Gallery,
Stephen White
Texts by Marjorie Allthorpe-Guyton, Susan Ferleger Brades and
Isobel Johnstone, assisted by Frances Munk
Entries compiled by Jill Constantine, Ann Jones, Frances Munk and
Julia Risness
Photography compilation by Frances Munk, assisted by Christie Coutin,
Isabel Finch and Henrike Ingenthron

The publisher has made every effort to contact all copyright holders. If
proper acknowledgement has not been made, we ask copyright holders to
contact the publisher.

ISBN 1 85332 230 X

This catalogue is not intended to be used for authentication or related
purposes. The South Bank Board accepts no liability for any errors or
omissions which the catalogue may inadvertently contain.

Hayward Gallery Publishing titles are distributed outside North and South
America by Cornerhouse Publications, 70 Oxford Street, Manchester
M1 5NH, UK
tel. 0161 200 1503; fax. 0161 200 1504;
email: publications@cornerhouse.org; www.cornerhouse.org/publications

For further information about works in the Arts Council Collection, please
write to Isobel Johnstone, Curator, Arts Council Collection, Hayward Gallery,
SBC, Royal Festival Hall, London SE1 8XX, UK.

Contents

Foreword

In 1996, the Arts Council Collection celebrated its fiftieth birthday, and a glance through the following pages reveals that artists in Britain have kept the Collection on its toes. This is a book full of work of provocation and surprise, as well as sustained achievement.

Buying works of art for a public collection is a responsibility that requires knowledge, diligence and tenacity, and we should like to thank the artists, writers and curators who have worked with us as purchasers over the last thirteen years. We are above all grateful to the artists whose work has been purchased, as their creativity makes the Collection what it is. We should also like to thank those artists who are not yet represented in the Collection, but who have submitted work for consideration. While sometimes our decisions may have brought disappointment, there is no doubt their work enriches and enlivens the visual arts in Britain, which are seeing unprecedented international success.

The Collection does not seek gifts, but in recent years particularly it has benefited from some exceptional generosity. Charles Saatchi has donated two outstanding groups of work, for which we are very grateful. We are also indebted to the Arnolfini Collection Trust and to several individual artists, including the late and sadly missed Prunella Clough, for the works that they have given.

The success of British artists can create problems for public collections with limited funds, especially as the price of new art escalates. In order to represent British achievements effectively and to enable work to be seen nation-wide, on occasion more expensive work is recommended for purchase. Thanks to The Henry Moore Foundation and the National Art Collections Fund, who have provided financial assistance in several notable cases, we have been able to bring major new work by established artists into the Collection.

We are grateful to Caroline Wetherilt, the Hayward's Art Publisher, who has supervised the production of this book with the ready help of Jonathan Jones, Publishing Co-ordinator. Its design is the work of Adam Hooper at Hoop Design, who has brought characteristic precision and flair to an exacting task. The compilation of images and texts has been the responsibility of Frances Munk and Julia Risness, whose patience and resourcefulness is greatly appreciated.

Acquiring work and managing the Collection entails collective effort. The warmest thanks are due to the staff of the Arts Council Collection: Curator, Isobel Johnstone; Assistant Curator, Jill Constantine; and Curator of Projects, Ann Jones, assisted by Frances Munk, Christie Coutin, Isabel Finch, Henrike Ingenthron and formerly by Ella O'Halloran. Together with the technical and transport team at the Hayward Gallery and with the particular involvement of the Collection's Senior Technician, Richard Nesham, and Fine Art Storeperson, Ryan Rodgers, works are ably looked after and, crucially, brought to a wide audience in this country and abroad, as the activities described overleaf make clear.

Marjorie Allthorpe-Guyton
Director, Visual Arts, Arts Council of England
Susan Ferleger Brades
Director, Hayward Gallery

Introduction

This volume of new works in the Arts Council Collection is the fourth in a series of catalogues listing acquisitions. It includes sculpture, painting, photography, video, film and installation, original works on paper, prints and multiples acquired between January 1989 and December 2002, and contains material published in the CD ROM of Acquisitions 1989-95 and in *The Saatchi Gift to the Arts Council Collection* of 2000.[1]

The Arts Council Collection, which is managed by the Hayward Gallery in London on behalf of the Arts Council of England, is the largest national loan collection of modern and contemporary British art in the world. This catalogue is essentially a reference book for borrowers and a starting point for study. It also provides an overview of recent achievements in British art, by senior artists and younger generations.

Art made in Britain has rarely shown such strength and variety as it has during the past decade. Its character is distinctive, much having been learnt from the example and teaching of innovative artists in the 1960s and 1970s such as Anthony Caro, Gilbert & George, Richard Hamilton, Phillip King, Richard Long and Bridget Riley, and the now famous sculptors emerging in the 1980s, among them Tony Cragg, Richard Deacon, Antony Gormley and Anish Kapoor. Another element is the vision and perspective brought to British culture by new generations from across the world, who have made the United Kingdom their home. A change in practice is the predominance of photography and video. When the first catalogue was published in 1980, most original works were paintings. Between 1972 and 1986 photography, largely documentary, was collected by a separate Arts Council committee. Video was also once supported separately. Now both media are an acknowledged part of visual arts practice and very much the concern of Collection purchasers alongside the recent growth of online digital art practice.

The Collection began when the Arts Council of Great Britain was founded in 1946, and took over a small group of paintings for tour. These had been purchased by CEMA, the Council for the Encouragement of Music and the Arts, during the Second World War. The intention was to educate as well as to entertain and, in the case of visual art, to show new and precious work outside London. It was anticipated that people might buy more art themselves and relieve the government of responsibility for its support and promotion. Although this isn't quite what happened – even today most contemporary British art is bought by collectors abroad – the Arts Council of England (as it became in 1996), has maintained its commitment and continues to support touring and the Collection. In the latter case, moderate investment has created a unique resource, one that continues to grow and to be more and more actively used. The total number of works in the Collection is now close to 7,400, including 1,500 paintings, 500 sculptures, 870 original works on paper, 400 mixed-media works, 1,850 artists' prints and multiples, 2,300 photographs and some 70 video, film and installation pieces.

The Collection aims to purchase innovative work from artists living in Britain.[2] In order to achieve this, a method of purchasing has evolved that maintains accountability and yet provides the freedom and flexibility essential to the successful pursuit of new art. Six individuals, usually an artist, a writer, a curator, the Director of the Arts Council of England's Visual Arts Department, the Director of the Hayward Gallery and the Curator of the Collection, purchase for eighteen months, after which new outside purchasers are appointed to allow a change of views. We are indebted to everyone who has been involved in this exacting process. Purchasers between 1989 and 2002 are listed on page 21.

Funds are currently approximately £152,000 per annum and have been at a similar level for nearly a decade, before which they were even less. Because of its limited budget, the Collection tends to concentrate on buying the work of younger emerging artists. Earlier it was possible to see an artist more fully-represented but this is now too costly in the case of successful artists and would mean limiting the range of artists included. There is a great amount to be seen – in London alone it is estimated that there are 13,500 artists – and the Collection must be aware of developments throughout the United Kingdom. Studios and many galleries are visited, and the vital role played by art dealers in finding and supporting artists is fully acknowledged. Artists in England may apply to have their work considered for purchase. This is generally done initially by sending in slides, which are viewed at purchasing meetings.

Occasionally, purchasers recommend an outstanding work by a mature artist. Such purchases can be very expensive and for them to succeed the Collection needs benefactors. We are greatly indebted to The Henry Moore Foundation and the National Art Collections Fund, both of whom contributed to the purchase of Richard Deacon's sculpture *Kiss and Tell*, 1989, and Antony Gormley's *Field for the British Isles*, 1993. The latter is the largest work yet bought, consisting as it does of 40,000 terracotta figures, but the Collection is uniquely able to make it available for loan. Since its acquisition in 1995, it has been shown in ten venues, including a train shed in Gateshead, a cathedral cloister in Salisbury and the Joseph Hotung Great Court Gallery at the British Museum, and seen by nearly half a million people. Further support was given by The Henry Moore Foundation towards the purchase of Damien Hirst's *He Tried to Internalise Everything*, 1992–94, and Anish Kapoor's *Untitled*, 1997–98, and by the National Art Collections Fund towards Richard Deacon's *Kind of Blue (A)*, 2001. Such financial contributions strengthen the Collection in ways that would not otherwise be possible and enable very special work to be seen throughout the country.

The remit of the Collection is to be out, and it is most visible in the regions. Although its handling base and offices are on the South Bank in London, in the Hayward Gallery and Royal Festival Hall, works from the Collection are rarely on view in the Hayward, the last time being in 1996 during the Arts Council Year of Visual Art when *ACE!*, a show of new purchases, and Antony Gormley's *Field for the British Isles*, came to London. These exhibitions were launched at the Hatton Gallery, Newcastle, and in the British Rail Greensfield Works, Gateshead, respectively. While future plans for the Hayward include a gallery for the Collection, this will provide a showcase only; we want works in the Collection to be actively circulated and out on loan.

Loans from the Collection fall into two main categories: exhibition loan and long loan. The Arts Council's exhibition touring service, for which the Collection was founded, remains one of the main vehicles for showing the works. This service, currently named National Touring Exhibitions, is also run by the Hayward Gallery. It creates and tours exhibitions that other venues might have difficulty in organizing because of cost and complexity, such as *Trauma*, initiated in collaboration with Dundee Contemporary Arts, *Cobra*, which was launched at BALTIC, Gateshead in March 2003 and the five-yearly *British Art Show*, which is the largest exhibition of recent British art to tour nationally. Collection exhibitions form a large part of the National Touring Exhibitions programme and are inexpensive for galleries to hire. Each year several Collection shows are made, and these tour on average for two years. They tend to be about subjects that emerge from what is being bought, like *Words*, a collaboration with Plymouth Museum and Art Gallery, about the use of text in art dating from 1932[3] to 2000, or *Bad Behaviour*, the first National Touring Exhibition to be shown at Longside in Yorkshire Sculpture Park, an exhibition of recent sculpture representing disruptive, non-formal trends. Sometimes, as in *Out of Line*, a range of work in a traditional medium (in this case, drawing) illuminates aspects of new practice. The Collection and National Touring Exhibitions enjoy a privileged position as part of the Hayward Gallery in London and benefit from its curatorial, public programmes, publishing, technical, press and marketing staff. Its transport fleet gives easy access nationally. Both rely on building relationships with curators in galleries throughout the country, who initiate exhibitions as well as house them.

Spotlights, a series begun in 1993, provide more flexibility for galleries with smaller spaces or who wish to make a loan the opportunity to change the focus of one of their own collection displays. These exhibitions consist of a group of works by one artist, for example *Kenneth Martin*, which began its tour at the Babylon Gallery, Ely, or of a single work, such as Douglas Gordon's *Croque Mort*, 2000, which began its tour at Wolverhampton Art Gallery in 2003. Smaller-scale cased exhibitions of works on paper and photographs travel to an even wider variety of venues, including libraries, schools and community art centres, and often tour continuously for five years or more. A list of Collection shows with catalogues since 1989, including all Spotlights, is given on page 20.

As it has grown, the Collection has become a loan resource for other venues making exhibitions in the United Kingdom. These loans range from one or two works to large groups of work and – in an increasing number of cases – whole exhibitions. Galleries using the Collection in this way since 2000 include the Peterborough Museum and Art Gallery; Mappin Art Gallery, Sheffield; Gardner Centre, Brighton; Newlyn Art Gallery, Penzance; York City Art Gallery; Orleans House, Twickenham; Oriel Mostyn, Llandudno;

Glynn Vivian Art Gallery, Swansea; Russell-Cotes Art Gallery and Museum, Bournemouth; and The Lowry, Salford. Most exhibition loans are free – borrowers have only to pay for transport and insurance although there is a small fee for loans abroad. There is also an administration charge for stand-alone displays. Such collaborations are especially welcome: Collection staff get to know their colleagues in regional museums and galleries, and curators there in turn gain a sense of ownership and understanding of the Collection, which encourages future use. In the last decade, the number of curators with knowledge of contemporary art has greatly increased, and there is a corresponding rise in the number of venues with suitable spaces. These changes are in part due to Arts Council initiatives: the MA course in curating and commissioning contemporary art at the Royal College of Art founded in association with Tate; Lottery-funded capital projects such as the New Walsall Art Gallery and BALTIC; the Contemporary Art Society project, also funded by the Lottery, to enable regional museums to purchase works by contemporary artists; and the rise of independent curators countrywide. Much has been achieved through the energy and enterprise of experienced exhibition curators, especially in the regions, convinced of the power of new art to attract audiences.[4] As its reputation for modern as well as contemporary art grows, the Collection receives more and more requests to lend to exhibitions abroad. These are often, but by no means exclusively, of work by well-established names.

The Collection's long-loan scheme provides loans for the museum sector but also, importantly, farther afield. Museums and galleries borrow the most valuable historical paintings and sculptures for displays of up to two years, a time limit imposed to ensure that key examples are able to circulate to those who would like to have them. A great effort is made to send art to places not generally associated with fine art, where people may encounter original works in the course of their normal lives. These long loans are generally for five years and go to non-commercial buildings, colleges, town halls and hospitals, provided the latter are buying art for themselves. Information is provided about all works that go out. To arrange a long-loan, Collection staff visit the venue to check possible locations and security, and the borrower is then invited to select work at a viewing in London. There is a one-off charge, which includes delivery and installation by Hayward Gallery transport and technicians. This is an important and developing area for the Collection, and there are currently long-loans in over one hundred venues.

Loans are also occasionally made to the corporate sector. In 1998, *Fifty Years of British Sculpture: Works from the Arts Council Collection* was organized by the NatWest group for their Lothbury Gallery. This was an unusual event because it was the first Collection show to be on view to the general public in the City of London, and it was a collaboration with a bank, NatWest, which at that time was still building their own art collection. Another collaboration is presently developing with Clifford Chance, participants in the Hayward Gallery Corporate Patrons scheme, with a view to making an annual display of paintings and sculpture in the public areas of their new premises at Heron Quays in Canary Wharf later in 2003.

The Collection has received several gifts. These include a fine Naum Gabo print from Nina Williams, on the occasion of the exhibition *Naum Gabo*, 1987–88, and a sculpture by Joan Moore from Kenneth Armitage. Stephen Farthing gave a large painting inspired by his residency during the Hayward's *Leonardo da Vinci* exhibition in 1989. Particularly welcome to friends and colleagues is the painting by Patrick George, *Portrait of Joanna Drew*, 1960–61, one of two gifts by Joanna Drew following her distinguished career as Director of Art at the Arts Council and Director of the Hayward Gallery. In the course of the preparation of her Spotlight, Prunella Clough, with characteristic generosity, donated four singular drawings. Her popular exhibition was still touring at the time of her death in 1999, and was to be seen at ten venues. Liam Gillick donated *Applied Complex Screen*, 2000, commissioned by the Hayward Gallery for its *Turnaround* series, a luminous work that is also practical for loan. Sonia Boyce gave the Collection *So Amazing*, 2000, an original design for an award for participants in the Hayward Gallery Public Programmes' initiative with the Department of Health, *Make it Happen in Art* (2001–02), and Barry Martin has given a study drawing for *Series Revelation – 'Tret'*. From the Lux Gallery, we received Elizabeth Wright's *Pizza Delivery Moped Enlarged to 145% of its Original Size*, 1997. We are most grateful to all these generous friends. The Collection has also been given earlier sculpture and paintings by Kate Blacker, Nigel Hall, Peter Sedgley, William Tillyer and John Virtue from the Arnolfini Collection Trust. These have in some cases filled gaps and, in others, enhanced existing representations. We would especially like to thank Jeremy Rees, founding Director of Arnolfini and Trustee of the Arnolfini Collection Trust, for this welcome donation.

Most spectacular and extensive of all recent gifts are those from Charles Saatchi, who donated one-hundred works of art by sixty-three artists in 1999 and has just made a second gift of thirty-four sculptures by eighteen artists. Charles Saatchi has been responsible for transforming public interest in contemporary art in Britain and abroad since he opened his gallery in London in the mid 1980s. His particular support and promotion of Young British Artists emerging at the end of that decade led to the 1990s' YBA phenomenon, culminating in the *Sensation* exhibition at the Royal Academy in 1997. Two years later, the Arts Council Collection was offered the first gift – a donation unprecedented in its scale. It was published as a separate catalogue and is also listed and illustrated here.[5] This includes work by fourteen artists who were in *Sensation*.[6] Its effect on the profile and use of the Collection was immediate. Museums and galleries asked for loans and made their own displays, among them the Mappin Art Gallery, Sheffield; Towner Art Gallery, Eastbourne; Bournemouth Institute; Shrewsbury Museum and Art Gallery; Talbot Rice Gallery, Edinburgh; Glasgow School of Art; and Usher Gallery, Lincoln. The second gift includes prominent names from the first gift, an original sculpture by Marc Quinn and works by newcomers to the Collection who have already exhibited quite widely. This gift will be published separately.[7] Its timing is perhaps propitious for both Charles Saatchi and the Hayward Gallery. Having closed his gallery in North London, at the time of writing Charles Saatchi is about to open a new space on London's South Bank. For the Collection, a new chapter begins when its sculpture moves to Yorkshire.

The Arts Council Collection is unique among the three national loan collections in having a large collection of sculpture. For practical reasons neither the British Council Collection, which is used to promote Britain outside the United Kingdom, nor the Government Art Collection, which is used for display in government offices in Britain and in British embassies abroad, has consistently acquired modern and contemporary three-dimensional work. In 2003, the sculptures and multiples in the Arts Council Collection move to a new home at Longside in Yorkshire Sculpture Park. Here, sculpture in the Collection will be displayed in twice-yearly exhibitions at Longside Gallery, in an annual programme that will be shared with Yorkshire Sculpture Park. Exemplary storage facilities, including a viewing room where borrowers will be able to see potential loans on demand, will ensure that proper care of sculpture will be combined with new visibility and opportunities for access. This project, which is funded by the Arts Council of England with the generous support of The Henry Moore Foundation, will further enhance Yorkshire's reputation as a unique centre for sculpture, and extend the national reach of the Collection and the Hayward.

With an established base in the regions, the Collection anticipates new opportunities for access and loan. In London, as counterpart to the improved situation for sculpture, there will be a new store for two-dimensional work, in a location where borrowers can make their selections more conveniently than has been possible for some time.

In conclusion, the Collection is planned to go on-line in 2003 and this book may be the last of its kind. It is appropriate to view it therefore not only as a useful means of access to a uniquely available resource, but as material evidence to celebrate the Collection now that it has reached its half-century. Most importantly, it pays tribute to all those artists whose unstoppable inventiveness makes the Collection a force for the future.

Isobel Johnstone
Curator, Arts Council Collection

Notes

1   Volume 1 *Arts Council Collection Acquisitions 1942–78* (1979), Volume 2 *Arts Council Collection Acquisitions 1979–83* (1984) and Volume 3 *Arts Council Collection Acquisitions 1984–88* (1988). London: Arts Council of Great Britain; CD ROM ACE: *Arts Council Collection Acquisitions 1989–95*. London: Arts Council of England, the South Bank Centre and Axis, 1988; *The Saatchi Gift to the Arts Council Collection*. London: Hayward Gallery Publishing, 2000.

2   In this catalogue there are prints and multiples by foreign artists. Early on in the history of the Arts Council Collection acquisitions were seen as an inexpensive way to represent foreign developments relevant to British practice. Since 2001, this policy has been discontinued in preference to concentrating limited resources on work made by artists living in the UK, and occasionally British artists living abroad.

3   Ben Nicholson's *Bocque* of 1932 was bought in 1950, when it was still normal to make occasional historical purchases, probably to fulfil the needs of an exhibition. This stopped in the 1960s as purchasing focussed exclusively on contemporary art.

4   On average 500 exhibition loans are made to 140 venues in Britain each year.

5   See note 1.

6   Artists in the Saatchi Gift of 1999 are: Liz Arnold, Alan Ball, Jordan Baseman, Richard Billingham, Terence Bond, Martin Boyce, Glenn Brown, Phil Brown, Simon Callery, Adam Chodzko, Daniel Coombs, Keith Coventry, Martin Creed, Peter Davis, Jeffrey Dennis, Rod Dickinson, Katharine Dowson, Simon English, Rachel Evans, Mark Fairnington, Rose Finn-Kelcey, Paul Finnegan, Mark Francis, John Frankland, Alison Gill, John Greenwood, Graham Gussin, Siobhán Hapaska, Alex Hartley, Claude Heath, Nicky Hirst, Louise Hopkins, John Isaacs, Chantal Joffe, Joanna Kirk, Darren Lago, Abigail Lane, Langlands & Bell, David Leapman, Marysia Lewandowska, Brad Lochore, Melanie Manchot, Nicholas May, Ian McLean, Stephen Murphy, Mariele Neudecker, Renato Niemis, Jonathan Parsons, Gary Perkins, Hadrian Pigott, Joanna Price, James Rielly, Gary Rough, Emma Rushton, Nina Saunders, Jane Simpson, Kerry Stewart, Marcus Taylor, Carina Weidle, John Wilkins, Richard Wilson, Lucy Wood and Richard Woods.

7   Artists in the Saatchi Gift of 2002 are: Jordan Baseman, Terence Bond, Mark Cannon, Ian Dawson, Paul Finnegan, John Frankland, Steven Gontarski, Gregory Green, Brian Griffiths, Siobhán Hapaska, Alex Hartley, Mark Hosking, John Isaacs, Hadrian Pigott, Marc Quinn, Nina Saunders, Gary Webb and Richard Wilson.

Arts Council Collection exhibition publications since 1989

Catalogues

Spotlight Series

This series is published to accompany exhibitions from the Arts Council Collection devoted to a single painting, sculpture, installation or group of works by an individual artist.

Purchasers

1988–89

Susan Ferleger Brades (Hayward Gallery), Isobel Johnstone (Arts Council Collection), John Lyons (artist), John Maine (artist), Roger Malbert (National Touring Exhibitions), Julia Peyton-Jones (Hayward Gallery), Sarah Wason (Arts Council of England), Boyd Webb (artist)

1990–92

Barry Barker (National Touring Exhibitions), Caroline Collier (National Touring Exhibitions), Noelle Goldman (Arts Council of England), Mel Gooding (writer and critic), Susan Hiller (artist), Isobel Johnstone (Arts Council Collection)

1992–94

Marjorie Allthorpe-Guyton (Arts Council of England), Colin Grigg (Arts Council of England), Greg Hilty (Hayward Gallery), Shirazeh Houshiary (artist), Isobel Johnstone (Arts Council Collection), Vong Phaophanit (artist), Adrian Searle (artist and critic)

1994–96

Marjorie Allthorpe-Guyton (Arts Council of England), Martin Caiger-Smith (Hayward Gallery), Isobel Johnstone (Arts Council Collection), Simon Linke (artist), Nima Poovaya-Smith (Keeper of Arts, Bradford Art Galleries and Museums), Richard Shone (critic and art historian)

1996–98

Marjorie Allthorpe-Guyton (Arts Council of England), Sacha Craddock (artist and critic), Susan Daniel-McElroy (Oriel Mostyn), Susan Ferleger Brades, (Hayward Gallery), Isobel Johnstone (Arts Council Collection), Cornelia Parker (artist)

1998–2000

Marjorie Allthorpe-Guyton (Arts Council of England), Guy Brett (writer and curator), Pavel Büchler (artist and lecturer), Susan Ferleger Brades (Hayward Gallery), Isobel Johnstone (Arts Council Collection), Yinka Shonibare (artist)

2000–02

Marjorie Allthorpe-Guyton (Arts Council of England), David Batchelor (artist and writer), Susan Ferleger Brades (Hayward Gallery), Isobel Johnstone (Arts Council Collection), Mariele Neudecker (artist and lecturer), Mark Sealy (Autograph, Association of Black Photographers)

2002–04

Marjorie Allthorpe-Guyton (Arts Council of England), Michael Archer (critic and lecturer), Susan Collins (artist and lecturer), Susan Ferleger Brades (Hayward Gallery), Keith Hartley (Scottish National Gallery of Modern Art), Isobel Johnstone (Arts Council Collection)

Notes on the entries and further information

Entries are arranged alphabetically by artist's name. In cases where an artist has more than one work in the Collection, works are arranged chronologically (and alphabetically within the same year). There are some exceptions to this ordering as a result of layout restrictions. Where works by the same artist have identical dates and titles, works are arranged according to accession number. Works involving more than one artist are cross-referenced. Portfolios of prints appear together and are cross-referenced under the artists' names. Within portfolios, works are arranged alphabetically by artist's name, unless the sequence of works is determined by the work itself. All works are illustrated, with the exception of some sets of photographs and prints.

The following details are given below each illustration:

Name of artist, date of birth (and death)
Title, date (photographs are dated by the published date, the printed date is included where known)
* Indicates that the series of works cannot be separated for display
Medium, given as fully as possible
The edition number of prints is given if known
Dimensions in centimetres, in the following order: height, width, depth
Weight (where significant)
Running time (where appropriate)
Name of individual or organization from whom the work was acquired, year of acquisition
Accession number
Copyright information if different from © the artist or estate of the artist 2003

Abbreviations

approx.	approximately
b.	born
c.	circa
ed.	edition
n.d.	not dated
no.	number

Further information

Initial inquiries regarding exhibition and long loans should be made to the Assistant Curator, Arts Council Collection, Hayward Gallery, London, SE1 8XZ. Tel: 020 7960 5217

Formal loan requests should be made in writing to the Curator, Arts Council Collection, Hayward Gallery, London, SE1 8XX

Catalogue

ABDU'ALLAH, Faisal b. 1969
The Last Supper, 1995
computer-generated bromide prints with selenium split tone, printed 2001;
2 parts, each 123 × 180; purchased from The Agency (Contemporary Art
Ltd.), 2001. ACC39/2001

AL-ANI, Jananne b. 1966
Untitled, 1998
c-type photographs, printed 1999; 2 parts, each 122 × 122; ed. 1/5;
purchased from the artist, 2001. ACC33/2000

ALLAN, Bruce b. 1950
Double Window, 1991
canvas, hardboard and wood; 143·6 × 317 × 7·6; purchased from the artist,
1991. ACC80/1991

ALLEN, Tim b. 1950
In the future, 1991
acrylic on canvas; 152 × 335; purchased from the artist, 1993. ACC12/1992

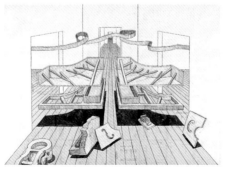

ALLINGTON, Edward b. 1951
Unfinished Instruments, 1989
ink and emulsion on paper on canvas; 152·4 × 213·2; purchased from the
artist, 1989. ACC45/1989

ALMOND, Darren
(see SCREEN portfolio)

ARNATT, Keith b. 1930
Untitled (from the *A.O.N.B.* series), 1982–84
gelatin silver print; 25·5 × 33; purchased from the artist, 2000.
ACC54/1999

ARNATT, Keith b. 1930
Untitled (from the *A.O.N.B.* series), 1982–84
gelatin silver print; 25·5 × 33; purchased from the artist, 2000.
ACC55/1999

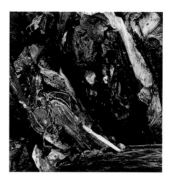

ARNATT, Keith b. 1930
Untitled (from the *Howlers Hill* series), 1987
c-type print, printed 1989; 61 × 61; purchased from Photographers' Gallery,
1989. ACC49/1989

ARNATT, Keith b. 1930
Untitled (from the *Pictures from a Rubbish Tip* series), 1988
c-type print; 58·5 × 72·5; purchased from Photographers' Gallery, 1989.
ACC47/1989

ARNATT, Keith b. 1930
Untitled (from the *Pictures from a Rubbish Tip* series), 1988
c-type print, printed 1989; 46·5 × 57; purchased from Photographers' Gallery,
1989. ACC48/1989

ARNOLD, Liz 1964–2001
Uncovered, 1995
acrylic on canvas; 122 × 76; gift of Charles Saatchi, 1999.
ACC140/1998

ARNOLD, Liz 1964–2001
Felicity, 1996
acrylic on canvas; 73 × 75; gift of Charles Saatchi, 1999.
ACC141/1998

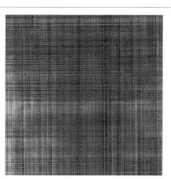

ARROWSMITH, Sue b. 1968
Pickett, 1996
ink and gesso on fibreboard; 183 × 183; purchased from Entwistle Gallery,
1997. ACC58/1996

ART & LANGUAGE
3 Maps, 1968–91 (detail)
cardboard; 5·4 × 24·6 × 32·6; unnumbered ed. of 100; purchased from ICA,
1994. ACC9/1997
© this edition: ICA, © original works: Art & Language 2003

AUSTEN, David b. 1960
Men Kill Sleeping Women, 1989
oil on canvas; 91·4 × 81·3; purchased from
Anthony Reynolds Gallery, 1991. ACC42/1991

AUSTEN, David b. 1960
On the Edge of Night, 1991
oil on canvas; 35·5 × 30·5; purchased from
Anthony Reynolds Gallery, 1991. ACC43/1991

AUSTEN, David b. 1960
City, 1999
oil on canvas; 167·5 × 152; purchased from Anthony Reynolds Gallery, 2000.
ACC64/1999

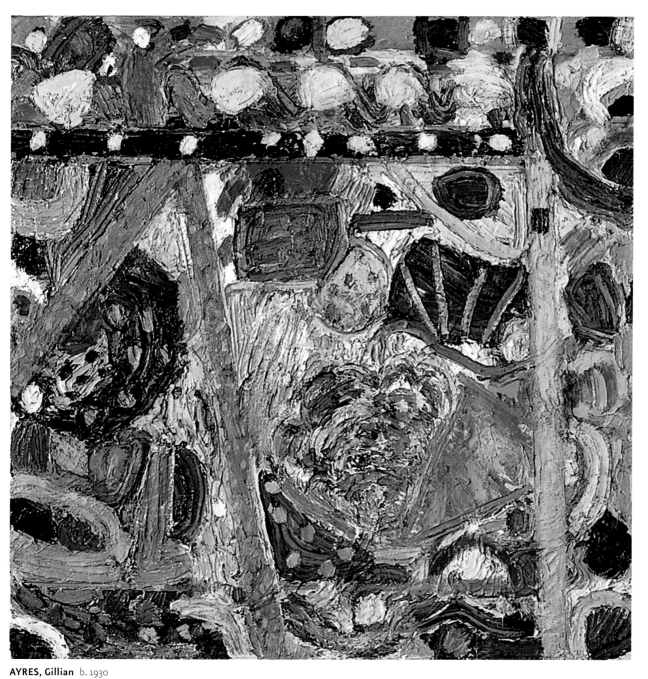

AYRES, Gillian b. 1930
Spica, 1989–90
oil on canvas; 183 × 183.7; purchased from Fischer Fine Art, 1991.
ACC44/1990

BAINBRIDGE, Eric b. 1955
In Heliotrope, 1990
fur fabric, fibreglass and plywood; 223·5 × 93·5 × 59; purchased from the artist, 1993. ACC12/1993

BALL, Alan b. 1962
Stress Fracture, 1994
acrylic on canvas; 157·5 × 175; gift of Charles Saatchi, 1999.
ACC252/1998

BALL, Alan b. 1962
Untitled (Sat 29/01/00), 2000
newsprint and correction fluid on canvas; 25·5 × 25·5; purchased from Mobile Home, 2000. ACC60/1999

BALL, Alan b. 1962
Untitled (Mon 7/02/00), 2000
newsprint and correction fluid on canvas; 25·5 × 25·5; purchased from Mobile Home, 2000. ACC71/1999

BALL, Alan b. 1962
Untitled (Wed 23/02/00), 2000
newsprint and correction fluid on canvas; 25·5 × 25·5; purchased from Mobile Home, 2000. ACC72/1999

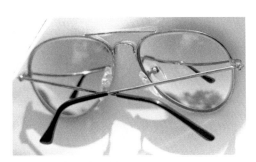

BANNER, Fiona b. 1966
Inside-Out Aviator Glasses, 1994
aluminium, mirrored glass; 6·5 × 14·5 × 14·5; ed. 3/50; purchased from Sarah Staton, 1994. ACC10/1997

BANNER, Fiona b. 1966
The desert, 1994–95 (installation shot)
screenprint; 6 parts, total 235 × 518·5; ed. 2/5; purchased from Frith Street Gallery, 2001. ACC23/2001

BANNER, Fiona b. 1966
Trance, 1997
22 audio tapes, drawing, plastic box; 23 × 16·5 × 9; running time: 20 hours; ed. 3/10; purchased from Frith Street Gallery, 1997. ACC6/1997

BANNER, Fiona
(see also BUGS portfolio)

BARBIERI, Olivo b. 1954
Legnago, 1986
c-type print; 24 × 41; purchased from the artist, 1998. ACC47/1990

BARCLAY, Claire b. 1968
Anodyne, 1994
cotton fabric, leather and feathers; pillows: 10·8 × 38·6 × 29·1, strap: 13·2 × 31 × 32·7; unlimited edition; purchased from the artist, 1994. ACC39/1997

BARCLAY, Claire b. 1968
Untitled (pole with shaved-off bristles), 1994
wood (pine) and mixed fibre bristle; 224 long, 3·5 diameter; purchased from the artist, 1997. ACC56/1996

BARCLAY, Claire b. 1968
Untitled (leather helmet cap), 1996
leather and thread; 25 × 25 × 25; purchased from the artist, 1997. ACC57/1996

BARCLAY, Claire b. 1968
Untitled (turned pole), 1996
wood (myrtle); 148 long, 3·5 diameter; purchased from the artist, 1997. ACC55/1996

BASEMAN, Jordan b. 1960
Closer to the Heart, 1994
cotton, human hair and metal; 40 × 70 × 3; gift of Charles Saatchi, 2002. ACC17/2002

BASEMAN, Jordan b. 1960
I have to love you but I don't have to like you, 1996
(installation shot)
human hair attached to wall; dimensions variable; gift of Charles Saatchi, 1999. ACC143/1998

BASEMAN, Jordan b. 1960
Pretty Baby, 1994
cotton, leather, plastic, hair; 48 × 14 × 6; gift of Charles Saatchi, 1999. ACC142/1998

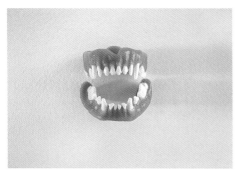

BASEMAN, Jordan b. 1960
Based on Actual Events, 1995
dogs' teeth, dental acrylic; 6 × 7 × 9; gift of Charles Saatchi, 2002.
ACC18/2002

BASEMAN, Jordan b. 1960
Boy, 1995
cotton and metal; 103 × 67 × 2·5; gift of Charles Saatchi, 1999.
ACC144/1998

BASEMAN, Jordan b. 1960
Moist Secret, 1995
wax and oil; 6 × 6 × 3; gift of Charles Saatchi, 2002.
ACC19/2002

BASEMAN, Jordan b. 1960
Up, Up and Away, 1995
metal, teeth and dental acrylic; 2 parts, each 3 × 4 × 3; gift of
Charles Saatchi, 2002. ACC20/2002

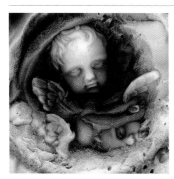

BEAN, Anne b. 1950
Under My Breath, 1994 (detail)
r-type print, printed 1998; 3 parts, total 33 × 93; purchased from the artist,
1999. ACC51/1999

BATCHELOR, David b. 1955
I Love King's Cross and King's Cross Loves Me, 5, 2001
metal, acrylic and enamel paint; dimensions variable; purchased from
Anthony Wilkinson, 2002. ACC16/2002

BEATTIE, Basil b. 1935
Imagine If, 1993
oil and wax on canvas; 259·5 × 304·7; purchased from Maak Gallery, 1994.
ACC25/1994

BEDDINGTON, Sarah b. 1964
Forty Nights, 2001 (1 of 7 works)
from a series of 40 paintings; oil on canvas; 7 works, each 25·5 × 34·5;
purchased from Hales Gallery, 2001. ACC15–21/2001

BELL, Nikki
(see LANGLANDS & BELL)

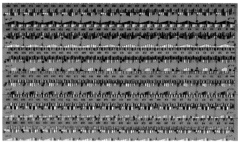

BELLINGHAM, David b. 1966
Ruler Painting (blue), 1994
enamel and plastic; 18·1 × 31·7; purchased from the artist, 1997.
ACC60/1996

BERGER, Adri b. 1960
Untitled (woman on horse with beach huts and trees), 1992
(1 of 2 works)
black-and-white photograph; 2 works, each 40 × 50; ed. 1/5; donated from
the exhibition *Image '90s*, 1992. ACC59–60/1993

BERNARD, Bruce 1928–2000
Lucian Freud with painting of Leigh Bowery, 1990
bromide print, printed 1990; 33 × 48·5; ed. 5/25; purchased from Peralta
Pictures, 1995. ACC30/1995

BERNARD, Bruce 1928–2000
*Leigh Bowery and Nicola Bateman posing for 'And for the
Bridegroom' (1)*, 1993
c-type print; 30·3 × 45·7; ed. 8/25; purchased from Peralta Pictures, 1995.
ACC32/1995

BERNARD, Bruce 1928–2000
*Leigh Bowery posing with painting (vertical) by
Lucian Freud*, 1994
c-type print, printed 1995; 45·8 × 31·4; ed. 4/25; purchased from
Peralta Pictures, 1995. ACC31/1995

BERNARD, Bruce 1928–2000
Sue Tilley posing in Lucian Freud's studio, 1995
c-type print; 30·9 × 45·8; ed. 2/25; purchased from Peralta Pictures, 1995.
ACC33/1995

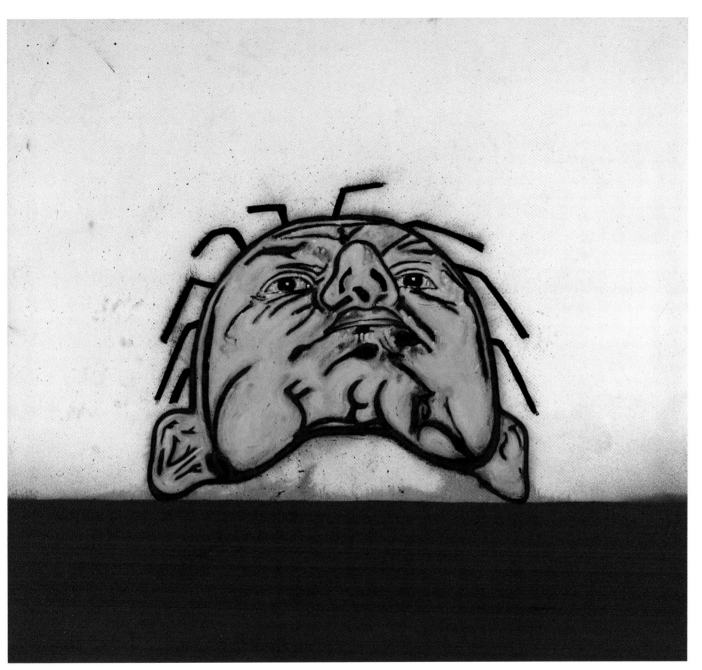

BEVAN, Tony b. 1951
Head Horizon, 1996
acrylic on canvas; 157 × 171; purchased from Theo Waddington
Fine Art Ltd., 1996. ACC10/1996

BHIMJI, Zarina b. 1963
Untitled, 1989
Polaroid photograph; 80 × 60; purchased from the artist, 1991.
ACC24/1990

BILLINGHAM, Richard b. 1970
Untitled (RAL 13), 1994
SFA4 colour photograph on aluminium; 105 × 158; ed. 2/5; purchased from
Anthony Reynolds Gallery, 1997. ACC23/1996

BHIMJI, Zarina b. 1963
Here was Uganda, as if in the vastness of India, 1999–2001
cibachrome on aluminium; 122·4 × 173·4; ed. 2/3; purchased from
Norwich Gallery, 2001. ACC40/2001

BILLINGHAM, Richard b. 1970
Untitled (RAL 50), 1994
SFA4 colour photograph on aluminium; 80 × 120; ed. 2/7; purchased from
Anthony Reynolds Gallery, 1997. ACC25/1996

BILLINGHAM, Richard b. 1970
Untitled (RAL 47), 1995
SFA4 colour photograph on aluminium; 120 × 80; gift of
Charles Saatchi, 1999. ACC147/1998

BILLINGHAM, Richard b. 1970
Untitled (RAL 49), 1995
SFA4 colour photograph on aluminium; 50 × 75; ed. 6/10; purchased from
Anthony Reynolds Gallery, 1997. ACC24/1996

BLACKER, Kate b. 1955
Local Lady, Local Landscape, 1983
corrugated metal and paint; 165 × 325 × 152; gift of Arnolfini Collection
Trust, 2000. ACC66/2000

BOHM, Dorothy b. 1924
Chair and Sprayed Wall, Downtown Cairo (Egypt), 1986
photograph, printed 1987; 40·5 × 30·5; purchased from the artist, 1988.
ACC48/1990

BOND, Henry b. 1966 and **GILLICK, Liam** b. 1964
*11th February 1992; Evacuation and closure of Whitehall and
surrounding area due to discovery of suspected device. Trafalgar
Square*, 1992
r-type photograph and text; photograph 49 × 67, text 30 × 21; purchased
from the artists, 1993. ACC6/1993

BOND, Henry b. 1966 and **GILLICK, Liam** b. 1964
*14th February 1992; Auction of the contents of Robert Maxwell's
London home, Sotheby's*, 1992
r-type photograph and text; photograph 49 × 67, text 30 × 21; purchased
from the artists, 1993. ACC5/1993

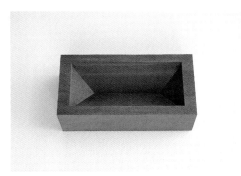

BOND, Henry
(see also OTHER MEN'S FLOWERS portfolio)

BOND, Terence b. 1960
Untitled (Brick), 1989
brick, dyed wood veneer on plywood and paint; 12 × 21·5 × 10·7; gift of
Charles Saatchi, 2002. ACC21/2002

BOND, Terence b. 1960
Solids, 1990
dyed wood veneer on plywood; 5 parts, each 12 × 12 × 11·2, overall length
439; gift of Charles Saatchi, 1999. ACC145/1998

BOND, Terence b. 1960
Flash Art, 1995 (installation shot)
linoleum/vinyl; 6 parts, total 240 × 240; gift of Charles Saatchi, 2002.
ACC22/2002

BOND, Terence b. 1960
Untitled, 1995
coconut fibre and ink; 46 × 76 × 4; gift of Charles Saatchi, 2002.
ACC23/2002

BONVIN, Susan b. 1948
Adrift, 1991
oil on canvas and wood; 66 × 62 × 19·6; purchased from the artist, 1991.
ACC75/1991

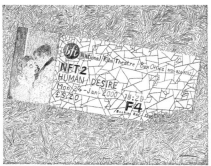

BORLAND, Christine b. 1965
Blanket Used on Police Firing Range, Berlin: Repaired, 1993
wool; 182·9 × 142·2; purchased from the artist, 1995. ACC2/1995

BORLAND, Christine b. 1965
Carrier, 1994
de-activated gun, polythene; 51 × 21 × 3·2; unlimited edition; purchased
from the artist, 1994. ACC40/1997

BOSHIER, Derek b. 1937
National Film Theatre, 2000
graphite on paper; 31 × 38; purchased from Shakespeare Fine Art, 2000.
ACC68/1999

BOWLING, Frank b. 1936
Great Thames IV, 1988–89
acrylic on canvas; 181 × 321; purchased from the artist, 1991. ACC8/1990

BOYCE, Martin b. 1967
Souvenir Placards (Standard Edition), 1993 (installation shot)
wood, emulsion and gloss; dimensions variable; gift of Charles Saatchi, 1999.
ACC148/1998

BOYCE, Sonia b. 1962
Mr close-friend-of-the-family pays a visit whilst everyone else is out, 1985
charcoal on paper; 109·2 × 150; purchased from the artist, 1989.
ACC32/1989

BOYCE, Sonia b. 1962
Lay back, keep quiet and think of what made Britain so great, 1986
charcoal, pastel and watercolour on paper; 4 parts, each 152·5 × 65;
purchased from the artist, 1989. ACC16/1989

BOYCE, Sonia b. 1962
So amazing, 2002
acrylic on paper; paper 51·8 × 51·8; gift of the artist, 2002; Print for participants in the Hayward/Department of Health programme 'Make it Happen in
Art', 2001–02, with young people looked after by Social Services. ACC14/2002

BRADBURY, Sarah b. 1971
Chairs, 1999 (installation shot)
clay, garden wire, enamel paint; 180 parts, each 6 × 3 × 4; purchased from
the Annual Programme, Salford, 2000. ACC40/1999

BREAKWELL, Ian b. 1943
The Elusive State of Happiness, 1979
newsprint and photograph; 59 × 46; purchased from Anthony Reynolds
Gallery, 2000. ACC66/1999

BREAKWELL, Ian b. 1943
No One Can Tell, 1993
photograph; 2 parts, each 299 × 183; purchased from Anthony Reynolds
Gallery, 1999. ACC13/1999

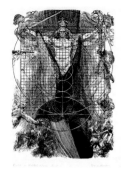

BRETT, Simon b. 1943
Exiles (from illustrations to *Hobbe's Whale, Poems by John Gohorry*), 1988
wood engraving; 17·7 × 12·4; ed. 15/50; purchased from the artist, 1993. ACC114/1997

BRISLEY, Stuart
(see OTHER MEN'S FLOWERS portfolio)

BROWN, Don
(see OTHER MEN'S FLOWERS portfolio)

BROWN, Glenn b. 1966
Decline and Fall, 1995
oil on canvas on board; 58·4 × 54·6; purchased from Karsten Schubert, 1995. ACC9/1995

BROWN, Glenn b. 1966
Exercise One, 1995 (detail)
c-type print; 5 parts, each 192 × 139; ed. 1/1; gift of Charles Saatchi, 1999. ACC146/1998

BROWN, Jemima b. 1971
Jemima and Dolly Present "Yes We Have No Bananas", 1999 (still)
Betacam sp installation, two monitors; running time: 4 minutes; ed. 2/3; purchased from the artist, 2000. ACC18/2000

BROWN, Phil b. 1972
Untitled (hand), 1994
silicone and plaster; 55 × 32 × 22; gift of Charles Saatchi, 1999. ACC149/1998

BUCHANAN, Roderick b. 1965
Chasing 1000, 1994 (still)
Betacam sp video tape; running time: 1 hour 30 minutes; ed. 2/6; purchased from the artist, 1997. ACC61/1996

BÜCHLER, Pavel b. 1952
How to Find a Way in the Dark, A–Z, 1983–84 (detail)
felt-tip pen on paper; 28 parts, each 30 × 24; purchased from Portfolio Gallery, 1998. ACC64–104/1997

BUGS PORTFOLIO ed. 20/90; purchased from the Byam Shaw School of Art, 2001

left to right, top to bottom

BANNER, Fiona b. 1966
Swarm, 2000
etching; image 23 × 18·1, paper 41 × 30·5. ACC42/2001

DEAN, Tacita b. 1965
Wasp, 2000
c-type print; 30·5 × 40·8. ACC43/2001

DOIG, Peter b. 1959
Kings Cross Mosquito, 2000
etching, sugar lift and drypoint; image 13·9 × 18·8, paper 30·6 × 40·5. ACC44/2001

GALLACCIO, Anya b. 1963
Spider's Leg at 400x, 2000
silver gelatin print; image 24·8 × 20·2, paper 40·4 × 30·3. ACC45/2001

LOCHORE, Brad b. 1960
Night Moth, 2000
digital archival ink jet print; image 26·7 × 37·1, paper 30·5 × 40·5. ACC46/2001

PARKER, Cornelia b. 1956
The Spider that died in the Tower of London, 2000
digital archival ink jet print; 30·3 × 40·5. ACC47/2001

PRENDERGAST, Kathy b. 1958
Mittens and Moth Eggs, 2000
digital archival ink jet print; image 19 × 28, paper 30·3 × 40·5. ACC48/2001

SHONIBARE, Yinka b. 1962
Grain Weevil, 2000
offset lithograph with gloss spot UV varnish; 30·5 × 40·5. ACC49/2001

TURK, Gavin b. 1967
Metamorphosis, 2000
lithograph; image 35·5 × 25, paper 40·5 × 26. ACC50/2001

WALLINGER, Mark b. 1959
King Edward and the Colorado Beetle, 2000
potato print; 1 from a series of 105 unique prints; 40·6 × 30·5. ACC51/2001

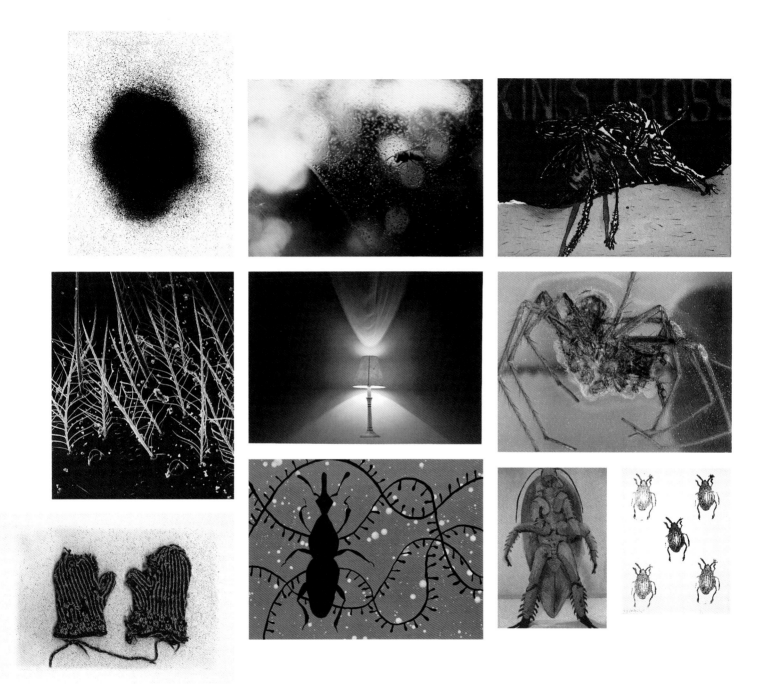

BULLOCH, Angela b.1966
Pink Chance Corner, 1990
perspex, glass, metal, electric light and plastic (kinetic); 2 spheres, each 30 in
diameter; purchased from Interim Art, 1993. ACC9/1992

BULLOCH, Angela b.1966
From the Eiffel Tower to the Risenrad, 1995 (still)
VHS video; running time: 34 minutes; unlimited edition; purchased from
Robert Prime Gallery, 1998. ACC68/1997

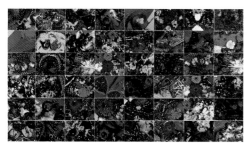

BURMAN, Chila Kumari b. 1957
A Moment to Herself, 2002
laser print; 152·4 × 208·2; purchased from the artist, 2002. ACC9/2002

BUTLER, Christine
(see DAHN, Walter)

CALLE, Sophie b. 1953
The Tie, 1993
silk; 139 × 8·7; ed. 1/150; purchased from Parkett, 1994. ACC11/1997

CALLERY, Simon b. 1960
Borough and Trinity, 1993
oil and oil pastel on canvas; 259·5 × 366; gift of Charles Saatchi, 1999.
ACC150/1998

CANNON, Mark b. 1972
Shelved IV, 1995
steel; 2 parts, each 130 × 96 × 13; gift of Charles Saatchi, 2002.
ACC24/2002

CARTER, Tony b. 1943
Pressure Point 1, 1987–88
MDF, aluminium, steel, gold, leather and paint; 236·2 × 162·6 × 21·6;
purchased from Anthony Reynolds Gallery, 1989. ACC50/1989

CASTRO, Lourdes b. 1930
White Shadow, 1969
screen print on layered acrylic; 49·8 × 39·8; purchased from
the artist, 1994. ACC24/1994

CATTELAN, Maurizio b. 1960
AC Forniture Sud, 1991
photograph, perspex, metal and nylon; 18 × 23 × 18; ed. 8/15; purchased
from Laure Genillard Gallery, 1994. ACC12/1997

CAULFIELD, Patrick h. 1936
Registry Office, 1997
acrylic on canvas; 92·1 × 76·8; purchased from Waddington Galleries, 1997.
ACC52/1997
© Patrick Caulfield 2003. All Rights Reserved, DACS.

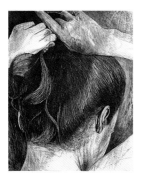

CAWKWELL, Sarah b. 1950
Putting My Hair Up, 1992
charcoal on paper; 150 × 120; purchased from the artist, 1993.
ACC7/1993

CHADWICK, Helen 1953–96
The Philosopher's Fear of Flesh No.1, 1989
cibachrome transparency, wood, perspex and metal; 154 × 52 × 14;
ed. 1/3; purchased from Marlene Eleini Gallery, 1989. ACC29/1989

CHADWICK, Helen
(see also OTHER MEN'S FLOWERS portfolio)

CHADWICK, Lynn b. 1914
Cloaked Couple 1, 1977
bronze; 51 × 45 × 37; ed. 1/8; exchanged by the artist for
The Fisheater (purchased 1951), 1986. ACC18/1985

CHAMBERS, Stephen b. 1960
This is a Woman You Know Well, 1994–95
oil on canvas; 152.5 × 183; purchased from Flowers East, 1996.
ACC12/1996

CHANDRA, Mohini b. 1964
Album Pacifica 1, 1997 (installation shot)
photographs printed on fibre, hand finished with wax and toner; 100 parts,
each 25 × 20 or 20 × 25; purchased from the artist, 2001. ACC53/2000

CHAPMAN, Jake and **Dinos**
(see SCREEN portfolio)

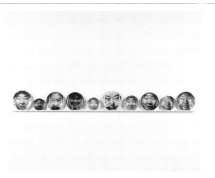

CHEUNG, Lisa b. 1969
I Want to be More Chinese, 1997
photo-emulsion on ceramic; 10 parts, each 25 diameter; purchased
from Whitechapel Art Gallery, 1998. ACC1/1998

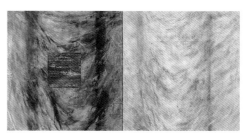

CHEVSKA, Maria b. 1948
Convulsive Cloak, 1989–90
oil and encaustic on linen and canvas; 2 parts, total 169.7 × 335.6; purchased
from Anderson O'Day Gallery, 1990. ACC4/1990

CHODZKO, Adam b. 1965
2101 Km/Hr (Secretor), 9468 Km/Hr (Secretor) and *9605 Km/Hr (Secretor)*, 1993 (2 works illustrated)
manifestation juice (food dye and glycerine), lead crystal, plastic, acrylic and acetate; 3 works: 36.5 x 12.3 x 5.3, 29.5 x 10.5 x 5.7 and 34 x 12 x 3; gift of Charles Saatchi, 1999. ACC151–153/1998

CHODZKO, Adam b. 1965
Untitled Stile (teenage version), 1992 (installation shot)
gloss paint and wood; 130.7 × 105.4 × 74; purchased from the artist, 1994.
ACC11/1993

CHUBB, Shirley b. 1959
Change, 1991
acrylic, PVA and paper on canvas; 112·5 × 112; purchased from
the artist, 1991. ACC45/1991

CHUBB, Shirley b. 1959
Heat, 1994 (installation shot)
metal, fire lighter and cane; 10·6 × 16·2 × 15; unnumbered ed. of 99;
purchased from the artist, 1994. ACC41/1997

CHUHAN, Jagjit b. 1955
Self Portrait, 1995
oil on canvas; 210 × 150; purchased from the artist.
ACC40/1995

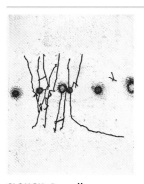

CLOUGH, Prunella 1919–99
Off the Tracks, 1977
etching, printed c.1982; image 25·5 × 20·5, paper 57 × 43; ed. 6/10;
purchased from the artist, 1999. ACC17/1999

CLOUGH, Prunella 1919–99
Tree, 1980
collage on paper; 56 × 53; gift of the artist, 1999.
ACC22/1999

CLOUGH, Prunella 1919–99
Double Shadow, 1992
charcoal on paper; 40 × 64; gift of the artist, 1999.
ACC21/1999

CLOUGH, Prunella 1919–99
Spine, 1992
chalk on lithographic proof; 65·5 × 53·5; gift of the artist, 1999.
ACC20/1999

CLOUGH, Prunella 1919–99
Device, 1996
etching; image 29·5 × 19·5, paper 51 × 38; ed. 7/25; purchased from
the artist, 1999. ACC19/1999

CLOUGH, Prunella 1919–99
Glassy, 1996
etching; image 24·5 × 29, paper 43·5 × 48·5; ed. 7/25; purchased from
the artist, 1999. ACC18/1999

CLOUGH, Prunella 1919–99
Samples, 1997
oil on canvas; 131·5 × 119·6; purchased from Annely Juda Fine Art, 1999.
ACC27/1998

CLOUGH, Prunella 1919–99
Creeper, 1998
etching; image 25·5 × 20·5, paper 43 × 35·5; ed. 2/25;
purchased from the artist, 1999. ACC16/1999

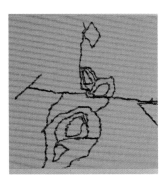

CLOUGH, Prunella 1919–99
Vegetation, 1999
ink on corrugated paper; 51·5 × 54·5; gift of the artist, 1999.
ACC23/1999

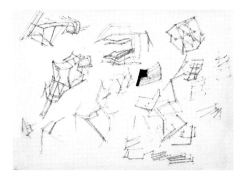

COBB, John b. 1946
Sketchbook Drawing, 1977
ink on paper; 23 × 29 (double-sided); purchased from the artist, 1989.
ACC38/1989

COBB, John b. 1946
Sketchbook Drawing, 1977
ink on paper; 40 × 51 (double-sided); purchased from the artist, 1989.
ACC39/1989

COBB, John b. 1946
Sketchbook Drawing, 1977
ink on paper; 23 × 29 (double-sided); purchased from the artist, 1989.
ACC40/1989

COBURN, Jason b. 1969
Push the Button, 1996
ink on paper; 29·8 × 21; purchased from Lotta Hammer, 1997.
ACC16/1996

COLDWELL, Paul b. 1952
Ladle and Funnel, 1989
bronze; 31 × 18 × 15; unique cast; purchased from the artist, 1991.
ACC27/1990

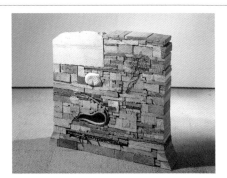

COLDWELL, Paul b. 1952
Bouquet, 1991
Portland stone, wood, marble, lead, paper and copper; 74 × 76 × 15;
purchased from the artist, 1991. ACC26/1990

COLDWELL, Paul b. 1952
My Father's Coat VI, 1996 (1 of 7 works)
etching; 7 works, each 76 × 56; ed. 1/10; purchased from the artist, 1997.
ACC31/1996 of a series ACC26–32/1996

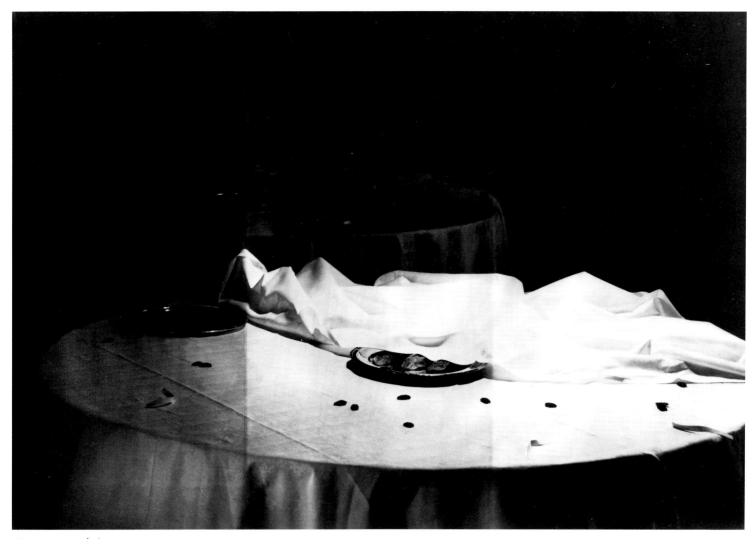

COLLINS, Hannah b. 1956
John Egan's Image: Tongues Without Words, 1988
black-and-white photograph; 203 × 304; ed. 1/2; purchased from ICA, 1989.
ACC15/1989

COLLISHAW, Mat
(see OTHER MEN'S FLOWERS portfolio and SCREEN portfolio)

COMPSTON, Joshua
(see OTHER MEN'S FLOWERS portfolio)

CONNEARN, David b. 1952
Coming-going, 1987
ink on paper; 203 × 203; purchased from the artist, 1994. ACC20/1994

CONSTABLE, Martin b. 1961
Untitled, 1992
oil on MDF; 54 × 46; purchased from Long & Ryle, 1992.
ACC3/1992

COOK, Ben b. 1967
Aerial view of the harbour, Marseilles (from the *Found Paintings* series), 1998
printed acrylic fabric; 145 × 145; purchased from the artist, 1999.
ACC125/1998

COOK, Ben b. 1967
Ode to Fontana (from the *Found Paintings* series), 1998
printed acrylic fabric; 144 × 144; purchased from the artist, 1999.
ACC124/1998

COOK, Richard b. 1947
Summer Morning, Lelant, 2000
oil on marine ply; 122 × 152; purchased from the artist, 2001. ACC28/2000

COOMBES, Andrew b. 1962
Let it be the Parkland, 1987
charcoal on paper; 109 × 81; purchased from the artist, 1991.
ACC25/1990

COOMBS, Daniel b. 1971
The Creation of the World, 1995
acrylic on canvas; 3 parts, each 210 × 210; gift of Charles Saatchi, 1999.
ACC154/1998

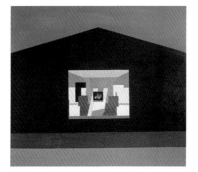

COOMBS, Daniel b. 1971
Night Bungalow I, 1995
acrylic on canvas; 213·3 × 243·8; gift of Charles Saatchi, 1999.
ACC155/1998

COOMBS, Daniel b. 1971
Night Bungalow II, 1996
acrylic on canvas; 213·3 × 243·8; gift of Charles Saatchi, 1999.
ACC156/1998

COOPER, Clement b. 1965
Hadley Cofie. Toxteth, Liverpool, 1994
black-and-white photograph; 20 × 16; purchased from Autograph, 1999.
ACC11/1999

COOPER, Clement b. 1965
Simeon Enticknap. Butetown, Cardiff, 1995
black-and-white photograph; 20 × 16; purchased from Autograph, 1999.
ACC10/1999

COOPER, Clement b. 1965
Arjan Singh. Ribbleton Ave Juniors, Deepdale, Preston, Lancs, 1998
black-and-white photograph; 20 × 16; purchased from Autograph, 1999.
ACC8/1999

COOPER, Clement b. 1965
Halima Valli. Deepdale Juniors, Deepdale, Preston, Lancs, 1998
black-and-white photograph; 20 × 16; purchased from Autograph, 1999.
ACC9/1999

COOPER, Thomas Joshua b. 1946
Mythic Stone: The Trossachs, 1983
selenium-toned gelatin silver print, printed 1988; 41·5 × 58; ed. 2/3;
purchased from Laure Genillard Gallery, 1991. ACC27/1991

COOPER, Thomas Joshua b. 1946
Mythic Stone Near Weatherville, Trinity County, California, 1984
selenium-toned gelatin silver print, printed 1988; 41·5 × 58; ed. 2/3;
purchased from Laure Genillard Gallery, 1991. ACC28/1991

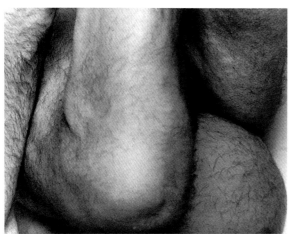

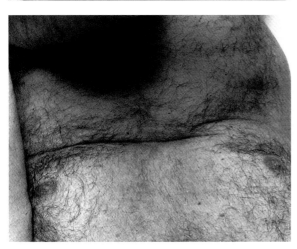

COPLANS, John b. 1920
Self Portrait (Upside Down No·1), 1992
gelatin silver print on aluminium; 3 parts, total 220 × 114·5; ed. 2/6;
purchased from London Projects, 1996. ACC9/1996

COUTTS, Marion b. 1964
For the Fallen, 2001
wood, suede and padding; 120 × 150 × 110; purchased from the artist,
2001. ACC2/2001

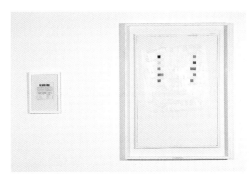

COVENTRY, Keith b. 1958
White Suprematist Painting, 1993
oil on canvas, painted wood and ink on paper; 2 parts, 125 × 97 × 7 and
33 × 28; purchased from Karsten Schubert, 1993. ACC14/1992

COVENTRY, Keith b. 1958
White Abstract (Ullein Reviesky, the last Deb), 1994
oil on canvas, wood, linen, gesso and glass; 74.9 × 59.7 × 5.7;
gift of Charles Saatchi, 1999. ACC157/1998

CRAIG-MARTIN, Michael b. 1941
History Painting, 1995
acrylic on canvas; 183 × 366; purchased from Waddington Galleries, 1995.
ACC25/1995

CREED, Martin b. 1968
Work No.11, 1989
brass and chrome-plated brass; 2 parts, each 5 diameter; purchased from the artist, 1995. ACC43/1995

CREED, Martin b. 1968
Work No.78, 1993
elastoplast, polystyrene, paper and cardboard; 2·2 × 6·8 × 4·9, box 10 × 10 × 10; no· 12 of an unlimited edition; purchased from Marc Jancou Gallery, 1994. ACC13/1997

CREED, Martin b. 1968
Work No.117, 1995
audio cassette; 10·8 × 6·9 × 1·7; running time: 1 minute; unlimited edition; purchased from the artist, 1995. ACC42/1995

CREED, Martin b. 1968
Work No.123, 1995
plastic, metal (sound); 3 parts, each height 4·6, diameter 9·3; gift of Charles Saatchi, 1999. ACC158/1998

CREED, Martin b. 1968
Work No. 135, 1996 (installation shot)
aluminium, cement, plaster and emulsion; 50·8 × 50·8 × 25·4; purchased from the artist, 1996. ACC41/1995

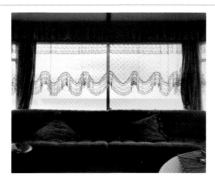

CRISP, Fiona b. 1966
TD8, 1999
photographic paper, MDF and coloured aluminium, printed 2000; 121 × 151; ed. 1/3; purchased from Matt's Gallery, 2001. ACC34/2000

CRISP, Fiona b. 1966
TD35, 1999
photographic paper, MDF and coloured aluminium, printed 2000; 121 × 151; ed. 1/3; purchased from Matt's Gallery, 2001. ACC35/2000

CRONE, David b. 1937
Summer Music, 1989
oil on canvas; 152 × 183; purchased from Fenderesky Gallery, 1991.
ACC12/1990

CROWE, Nick b.1968
Point 1, "It has to be an Elämys!" (from *The Ten Point Plan for a Better Helsinki*), 1998 (1 of 10 works)
black ink on paper; 10 works, each 70 × 100; purchased from the artist, 1999. ACC123/1998 and ACC254–262/1998

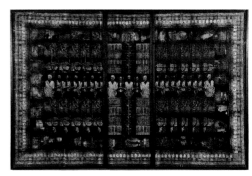

CRUMP, Simon b. 1960
Big Heat, 1989
mixed media collage; 181 × 275·5; purchased from the artist, 1989.
ACC46/1989

CRUZ, Juan b. 1970
Sancti Petri, 1998 (installation shot)
installation, 80 × 35mm slides, 1 audio cassette tape; running time: 35 minutes, 30 seconds; purchased from Matt's Gallery, 1998. ACC75/1997

CUDDIHY, Mikey b. 1952
Iron Gates of Life: Strength and Sweetness, 1991
acrylic and graphite on canvas; 236·5 × 178·2; purchased from Flowers East, 1991. ACC41/1991

CURRALL, Alan b. 1964
Sulky, 1993 (still)
Betacam sp video tape; running time: 1 minute, 20 seconds; ed. 2/5; purchased from the artist, 1997. ACC52/1996

CURRALL, Alan b. 1964
Jetsam, 1995 (still)
Betacam sp video tape; running time: 3 minutes, 47 seconds; ed. 2/5; purchased from the artist, 1997. ACC51/1996

CURRALL, Alan b. 1964
Telephone Conversation, 1995 (still)
Betacam sp video tape; running time: 4 minutes, 35 seconds; ed. 2/5; purchased from the artist, 1997. ACC53/1996

CURRALL, Alan b. 1964
Word Processing, 1995 (still)
Betacam sp video tape; running time: 6 minutes, 21 seconds; ed. 2/5 + 2; purchased from the artist, 1997. ACC54/1996

DADE, Adam b. 1975 and **HANNEY, Sonya** b. 1973
Stacked Hotel No·6, 2000 (still)
VHS video; running time: 235 minutes; ed. 1/5; purchased from the artists,
2001. ACC52/2000

DAHN, Walter b. 1954 **DROESE, Felix** b. 1950
STÜTTGEN, Johannes b. 1948 **BUTLER, Christine**
and **KRENKERS, Brigitte** b. 1956
Omnibus für Direkte Demokratie in Deutschland, 1990
plastic, metal, paint, copper and paper; 11·8 × 27·4 × 8·8; ed. 1/76;
purchased from Harry Ruhé, 1994. ACC14/1997

DALZIEL, Matthew b. 1957 and
SCULLION, Louise b. 1966
Television Cloth, 1994
aluminium and silk organza; 51 × 37 × 8; unlimited edition;
purchased from the artists, 1994. ACC42/1997

DALZIEL, Matthew b. 1957 and
SCULLION, Louise b. 1966
The Idea of North, 1998
compass in engraved perspex disc; 9 diameter; ed. 7/200;
purchased from The Multiple Store, 1999. ACC34/1998

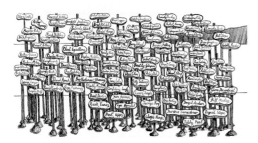

DANT, Adam b. 1967
Untitled 2, 1996
ink on paper; 131·4 × 236; purchased from the artist, 1997. ACC19/1996

DANT, Adam b. 1967
Untitled 4, 1996
ink on paper; 150 × 269·8; purchased from the artist, 1997. ACC20/1996

DANT, Adam b. 1967
Untitled, 1997
woodcut; image 62 × 43, paper 64 × 46; ed. 1/10;
purchased from the artist, 1997. ACC33/1996

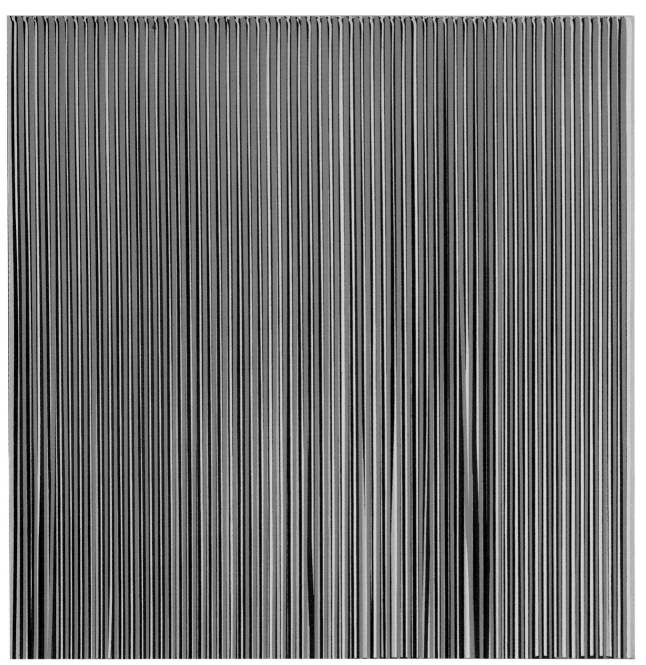

DAVENPORT, Ian b. 1966
Poured Lines: light orange, blue, yellow, dark green and orange, 1995
household paint on canvas; 213·4 × 213·4; purchased from Waddington Galleries,
1995. ACC38/1995

DAVEY, Grenville b. 1961
Eye: Pair A, 1993
screenprint; 2 parts, each 72 × 83.5; unnumbered ed. of 40;
purchased from The Paragon Press, 1994. ACC5/1994

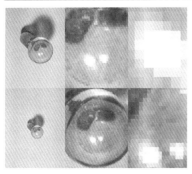
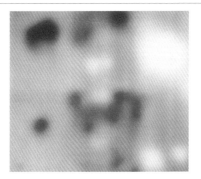

DAVEY, Grenville b. 1961
Eye: Pair B, 1993
screenprint; 2 parts, each 72 × 83.5; unnumbered ed. of 40;
purchased from The Paragon Press, 1994. ACC6/1994

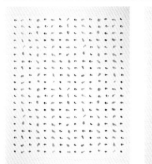
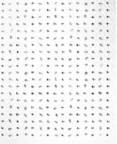

DAVEY, Grenville b. 1961
Eye: Pair C, 1993
screenprint; 2 parts each 83.5 × 72; unnumbered ed. of 40;
purchased from The Paragon Press, 1994. ACC4/1994

DAVEY, Grenville b. 1961
Eye, 1996
sugar-lift aquatint; 75.5 × 57.2; ed. 39/40; purchased from
Alan Cristea Gallery, 1997. ACC34/1996

DAVEY, Grenville b. 1961
Manubrium, 1994
painted steel and zinc coated steel; 2 parts: 42·5 × 90 × 90 and 139 × 90 × 90;
purchased from Lisson Gallery, 1994. ACC7/1994

DAVIES, John b. 1949
Elf Services Autoroute A26 Rumaucourt, 1988
bromide print; 38 × 56; purchased from the artist, 1993. ACC13/1993

DAVIES, John b. 1949
Canadian Memorial, Vimy, 1989
bromide print; 38 × 56; purchased from the artist, 1993. ACC14/1993

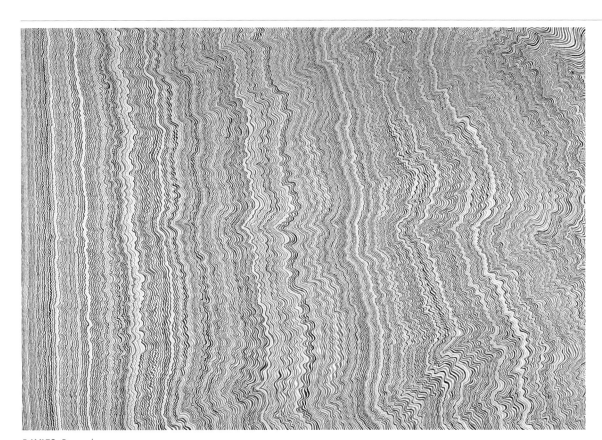

DAVIES, Peter b. 1970
Striped Painting, 1997
acrylic on canvas; 228·6 × 330·2; purchased from The Approach, 1998.
ACC73/1997

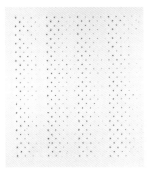

DAVIES, Tim b. 1960
Untitled Nail Drawing No. 3 Part I, 1998
scorched paper; 146.5 × 145.5; purchased from the artist, 1998.
ACC4/1998

DAVIES, Tim b. 1960
Untitled Nail Drawing No.3 Part II, 1998
scorched paper; 147.7 × 145.5; purchased from the artist, 1998.
ACC5/1998

DAVIS, Peter b. 1972
Untitled 3mm Blue – November 1995, 1995
gloss and satinwood on canvas; 99·6 × 208·8; gift of Charles Saatchi, 1999.
ACC159/1998

DAWSON, Ian b. 1969
171 Elements, 1998
various plastics; 160 × 160 × 230; gift of Charles Saatchi, 2002.
ACC25/2002

DAYAN, Eddie b. 1943
Symi/Greece, 1975 from the *Uneasy Landscapes* series, 1988–91
(1 of 11 works)
gelatin silver print, printed 1991; 11 works, 30·5 × 40·6, other dimensions
variable; ed. 2/30; purchased from the artist, 1991. ACC56–66/1991

DE MONCHAUX, Cathy b. 1960
Clearing the Tracks Before They Appear, 1994
steel, enamel, brass, muslin and ribbon; 77 diameter × 4 depth; ed. 1/3;
purchased from the artist, 1994. ACC43/1997

DEACON, Richard b. 1949
Kiss and Tell, 1989
epoxy resin, timber, plywood and steel; 175 × 233 × 162; purchased from
Lisson Gallery with assistance from The Henry Moore Foundation and the
National Art Collections Fund, 1990. ACC55/1989

DEACON, Richard b. 1949
Kind of Blue (A), 2001
ceramic; 149 × 102 × 80; purchased from Lisson Gallery wirh assistance from
the National Art Collections Fund, 2003. ACC51/2002

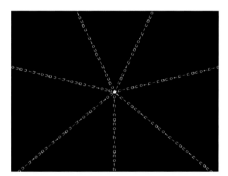

DEAN, Mark b. 1958
Ascension (nothing / Something Good), 1999
video projection; infinite loop; ed. 3/3; purchased from Laurent Delaye
Gallery, 2002. ACC52/2002

DEAN, Mark b. 1958
The Return of Jackie and Judy (+ Joey), 2001
video projection; infinite loop; ed. 1/3; purchased from Laurent Delaye
Gallery, 2002. ACC53/2002

DEAN, Tacita b. 1965
Delft Hydraulics, 1996 (still)
16mm black-and-white film with optical sound; projection size 36.5 × 48;
ed. 3/3; purchased from Frith Street Gallery, 2001. ACC31/2000

DEAN, Tacita
(see also BUGS portfolio)

DELARGY, Diarmuid b. 1958
Breda, 1990
oil on canvas; 183·4 × 121·3; purchased from
Fenderesky Gallery, 1991. ACC2/1991

DELLER, Jeremy b. 1966
The History of the World, 1998
screenprint; 66 × 112; ed. 37/100; purchased from Paul E. Stolper, 1998.
ACC6/1998

DELLER, Jeremy b. 1966
Karl Marx 18.12.2000, 2000
portfolio containing colour photographs, text, envelope and card; portfolio
74 × 48·3 × 3·3, 5 prints, each 30·5 × 40·6; ed. 1/5; purchased from Cabinet
Gallery, 2001. ACC70/2000

DENIS, Dominic
(see LONDON portfolio)

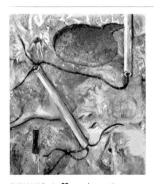

DENNIS, Jeffrey b. 1958
A Spy in the House of Frank, 1985
oil and charcoal on canvas; 114·3 × 99; gift of
Charles Saatchi, 1999. ACC160/1998

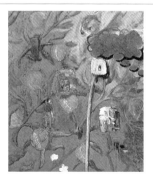

DENNIS, Jeffrey b. 1958
Strange Fruit, 1985
oil and charcoal on canvas; 86·4 × 74·4; gift of
Charles Saatchi, 1999. ACC161/1998

DENNIS, Jeffrey b. 1958
The Lost City, 1985
oil on canvas; 53·4 × 71; gift of Charles Saatchi, 1999. ACC162/1998

DERGES, Susan b. 1955
Untitled Sand Print, 1986 (1 of 7 works)
monotype, Japanese stone pigment on canvas; 7 works,
each 47·7 × 45·7; purchased from the artist, 1991.
ACC48–55/1991

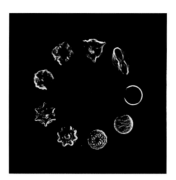

DERGES, Susan b. 1955
Hermetica, 1989
cibachrome print; 122 × 122; ed. 1/5; purchased from the artist, 1991.
ACC55/1991

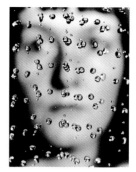

DERGES, Susan b. 1955
The Observer and the Observed, 1992
gelatin silver print; 90 × 73; purchased from the artist, 1993.
ACC15/1992

DI STEFANO, Arturo b. 1955
Kafka, 1987
woodcut; 77·8 × 62; artist's proof; purchased from the artist, 1993.
ACC113/1997

DIAMOND, Jessica b. 1957 **LE WITT, Sol** b. 1928
and **WEINER, Lawrence** b. 1940
Do-It-Yourself, 1993
mixed media; 30·5 × 26·7 × 2·5; unlimited edition; purchased from
IC Editions, 1994. ACC15/1997

DICKINSON, Rod b. 1965
Egg Bag, 1991
oil, dust, silicon and latex prosthetic on canvas; 213·5 × 183;
gift of Charles Saatchi, 1999. ACC163/1998

DICKINSON, Rod b. 1965
Venereal Daze, 1992
oil, dust, silicon and latex prosthetic on canvas; 213·5 × 183;
gift of Charles Saatchi, 1999. ACC164/1998

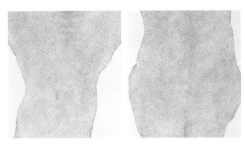

DIXON, Jane b. 1963
Untitled (torso diptych), 1997
graphite, absorbent ground and gesso on canvas; 2 parts, each 61 × 56;
purchased from the artist, 1997. ACC37/1996

DOHERTY, Willie b. 1959
Same Difference, 1990 (still)
slide projections and text; space required approx. 600 × 600; running time:
40-second sequence (repeated); purchased from Matt's Gallery, 1991.
ACC20/1990

DOHERTY, Willie b. 1959
At the End of the Day, 1994 (still)
Betacam sp video projection with sound; space required approx.
400 × 1200 × 500 ; running time: 3 minutes, 30 seconds; purchased from
Matt's Gallery, 1995. ACC11/1995

DOIG, Peter b. 1959
Red Deer, 1990
oil on canvas; 237·5 × 182·6; purchased from the artist, 1992. ACC86/1991

DOIG, Peter
(see also BUGS portfolio)

DOLVEN, Anne Katrine b. 1953
The Kiss, 2000 (still)
16mm film on DVD; projection size 160 × 120; running time: 7 minutes,
44 seconds; ed. 1/5; purchased from Anthony Wilkinson Gallery, 2001.
ACC22/2001

DONNELLY, Micky b. 1952
Olive, 1990
oil and pumice powder on canvas; 56·5 × 56·5; purchased from
Anderson O'Day Gallery, 1991. ACC73/1991

DONNELLY, Micky b. 1952
Landscape Painting No.5 (after Paul Henry), 1991
oil and pumice powder on canvas; 56·5 × 56·5; purchased from
Anderson O'Day Gallery, 1991. ACC72/1991

DORON, Itai
(see OTHER MEN'S FLOWERS portfolio)

DOWER, Natalie b. 1931
Sortie, 2001
oil on canvas on board; 36.1 × 36.1; purchased from Crane Kalman Gallery, 2001. ACC6/2001

DOWSON, Katharine b. 1962
Bubbling Glass, 1990
glass, water, wax, iron, air pump and plastic (sound); 94 × 152.5 × 96.5; gift of Charles Saatchi, 1999. ACC137/1998

DOWSON, Katharine b. 1962
Silicon Teats, 1992
silicon, glass, water and wood; 91.9 × 96.7 × 54.3; gift of Charles Saatchi, 1999. ACC138/1998

DRAGICEVIC, Milena b. 1965
Opet, 2002
oil on linen; 108.5 × 79; purchased from the artist, 2002. ACC4/2002

DRAPER, Kenneth b. 1944
Dark into Light, 1986
galvanized steel, wood, resin and colour pigment; 39 × 39 × 40; purchased from the artist, 1989. ACC26/1989

DROESE, Felix
(see DAHN, Walter)

ELLIOTT, Ashley b. 1974
A100-100 (Uniform White, Red, Ultramarine Blue), 1996
oil on canvas; 104.8 × 104.5 × 9.2; purchased from Jason & Rhodes, 1997. ACC45/1996

ELLIS, Peter b. 1955
Blank Firing, 1997
oil on canvas; 152 × 152; purchased from Anthony Wilkinson Gallery, 1998. ACC61/1997

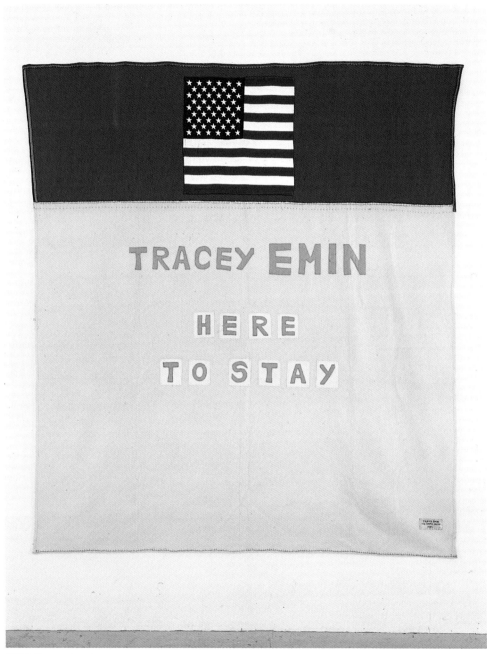

EMIN, Tracey b. 1963
The Simple Truth, 1995
wool, cotton and felt; 216 × 235; purchased from White Cube, 1998.
ACC74/1997

EMIN, Tracey b. 1963
Why I Never Became a Dancer, 1995 (still)
Betacam sp video tape on monitor or projected; running time: 6 minutes, 40
seconds; projection size 210 × 270; ed. 8/10; purchased from White Cube,
1998. ACC65/1997

EMIN, Tracey
(see also OTHER MEN'S FLOWERS portfolio)

ENGLISH, Simon b. 1959
Box II (Large), 1993
oil on canvas; 3 parts, total 200 × 600; gift of Charles Saatchi, 1999.
ACC165/1998

EVANS, Rachel b. 1965
'I was once asked at art college to write an essay on how it all began', 1995 (installation shot)
feather, quills, cotton and plasticine; 180 × 60 × 60; gift of Charles Saatchi, 1999. ACC166/1998

FAGEN, Graham b. 1966
Former and Form, 1993
concrete, wood, metal; 10 × 80 × 40; purchased from Matt's Gallery, 2000.
ACC41/1999

FAIRHURST, Angus
(see LONDON portfolio and OTHER MEN'S FLOWERS portfolio)

FAIRNINGTON, Mark b. 1957
The Greek Madonna, 1993
oil and gold leaf on panel; 60 × 44; gift of Charles Saatchi, 1999.
ACC167/1998

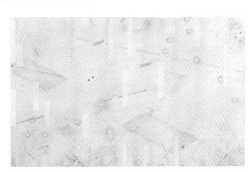

FARIAS, Oscar b. 1951
Nocturnal, 1987
wood engraving; 10 × 7.5; ed. 11/25; purchased from the artist, 1993.
ACC112/1997

FARRER, Julia b. 1950
Untitled, 1985
pencil and watercolour on paper; 57.5 × 90.2; purchased from Francis Graham-Dixon Gallery, 1992. ACC2/1992

FARRER, Julia b. 1950
Untitled, 1987
pencil, watercolour and gouache on paper; 24.8 × 60.8; purchased from Francis Graham-Dixon Gallery, 1992. ACC1/1992

FARTHING, Stephen b. 1950
Florence, 1989
oil on canvas; 173 × 207; gift of the artist from his residency at the Hayward
Gallery during the exhibition *Leonardo da Vinci*, 1989. ACC54/1989

FEENEY, Jacinta b. 1954
This Brief Transit, 1989
oil on canvas; 182·1 × 160; purchased from the artist, 1991.
ACC36/1991

FEND, Peter b. 1950
European Flag, 1992
cotton and wood; 41 × 31·5 × 6·3; ed. 1/300; purchased from
Marc Jancou Gallery, 1994. ACC16/1997

FESENMAIER, Helene b. 1937
Churnwood, 1990
pastel and paint on paper; 146 × 150; purchased from the artist, 1992.
ACC87/1991

FINN-KELCEY, Rose b. 1945
Steam Installation, 1992 (installation shot)
aluminium, water, steam; 350 × 350 × 200; gift of Charles Saatchi, 1999.
ACC171/1998

FINN-KELCEY, Rose b. 1945
Jolly God, 1997
wool, lime, latex and wood; 290 × 360 × 10; purchased from Camden Arts
Centre, 1998. ACC77/1997

FINNEGAN, Paul b. 1968
Car No.2, 1995 (installation shot)
r-type print; 72 × 105; gift of Charles Saatchi, 1999. ACC168/1998

FINNEGAN, Paul b. 1968
Spuriosis I, 1995
r-type print; 72 × 105; gift of Charles Saatchi, 1999. ACC169/1998

FINNEGAN, Paul b. 1968
Spuriosis II, 1995
r-type print; 72 × 105; gift of Charles Saatchi, 1999. ACC170/1998

FINNEGAN, Paul b. 1968
Untitled, 1995
resin, paint, leather and cotton; 185 × 140 × 90;
gift of Charles Saatchi, 2002. ACC26/2002

FINNEMORE, Peter b. 1963
God Dog Void Dog God, 1994
black-and-white photograph, selenium toned, printed 1995; 40·5 × 50·1;
ed. 2/12; purchased from the artist, 1997. ACC47/1996

FINNEMORE, Peter b. 1963
The Mocking of Christ, 1994
black-and-white photograph, selenium toned, printed 1995; 40·5 × 50·1;
ed. 2/12; purchased from the artist, 1997. ACC48/1996

FITZMAURICE, Leo b. 1963
Holland, 1995
acrylic on wood; 2 parts, each 5 × 14 × 5;
purchased from the artist, 1995. ACC18/1995

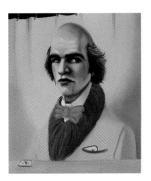

FLANNIGAN, Moyna b. 1963
The Last Minister, 2002
oil on canvas; 65 × 55; purchased from Dogger Fisher, 2002.
ACC54/2002

FLANNIGAN, Moyna b. 1963
Toujours la même chose, 2002
oil on canvas; 150 × 160; purchased from Dogger Fisher, 2002.
ACC55/2002

FLEURY, Sylvie b. 1961
Vital Perfection, 1993
cardboard and synthetic fur; 9·4 × 27·8 × 16·9; ed. 55/100;
purchased from Laure Genillard Gallery, 1994. ACC17/1997

FLOYER, Ceal b. 1968
Light, 1994 (installation shot)
glass, light fittings, flex, 35mm slides, projector; dimensions variable;
ed. 1/3; purchased from the artist, 1996. ACC7/1996

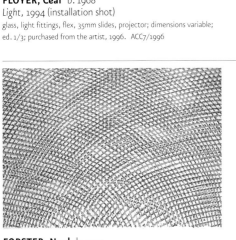

FORSTER, Noel b. 1932
Untitled, 1990–91
oil on linen; 152·5 × 213·5; purchased from the artist, 1998.
ACC60/1997

FORD, Laura b. 1961
Giraffe, 1998
plaster, steel and fabric; 370 × 500 × 100; purchased from
Camden Arts Centre, 1999. ACC15/1999

FORSTER, Peter b. 1934
The Rape of the Lock Canto III from *The Rape of the Lock* series,
1990
wood engraving; 17·8 × 11·4; ed. 30/30; purchased from the artist, 1993.
ACC111/1997

FOXCROFT, Lesley b. 1949
Untitled (vertical cardstack), 1991 (installation shot)
corrugated card; 350 × 35 × 12; purchased
from Laure Genillard Gallery, 1992. ACC91/1991

FRANCIS, Mark b. 1962
Positive, 1992
oil on canvas; 76 × 76; gift of Charles Saatchi, 1999.
ACC172/1998

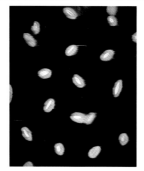

FRANCIS, Mark b. 1962
Untitled (Negative 2), 1992
oil on canvas; 107 × 91·5; gift of Charles Saatchi, 1999.
ACC173/1998

FRANKLAND, John b. 1961
You Can't Touch This, 1992–93 (installation shot)
laminated polythene and wood; dimensions variable;
gift of Charles Saatchi, 1999. ACC174/1998

FRANKLAND, John b. 1961
Ohne Titel, 1994
wood and gloss; approx. 500 × 250 × 250; gift of Charles Saatchi, 2002.
ACC27/2002

FRANKLAND, John b. 1961
Untitled 'Shed', 1994
laminated polythene and wood; 245 × 244 × 184; gift of Charles Saatchi,
2002. ACC28/2002

FRASER, Peter b. 1953
Triptych No·9, 1988
c-type photograph; 3 parts, each 117 × 117; ed. 1/2; purchased from
Interim Art, 1989. ACC37/1989

FRITSCH, Katharina b. 1956
Mill, Ambulance, Toads, 1990
vinyl; 3 parts, each 18 × 18; edition of 2,000;
purchased from Parkett, 1984. ACC18/1997

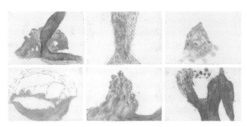

FROST, Judith b. 1956
Untitled (from the *Landmark* series), 1996
earth on paper; 6 works, each 48 × 68; purchased from the artist, 1998.
ACC14–19/1998

FROST, Terry b. 1915
Newlyn Blue Q, 1995
screenprint; image 73 × 73, paper 94·5 × 92; ed. 116/125;
purchased from Flowers East, 1998. ACC8/1998

FROST, Terry b. 1915
Zeus Flight, 1996
etching with aquatint; image 28·5 × 28, paper 48 × 45·5; ed. 22/45;
purchased from Flowers East, 1998. ACC7/1998

FRYDLENDER, Barry b. 1954
Young couple in front of an evening sky with traffic signs, 1987
c-type photograph; 36 × 50·6; purchased from the artist, 1990.
ACC49/1990

FULTON, Hamish b. 1946
Fourteen Works 1982–89, 1989
14 off-set lithographs; ed. 30/35; purchased from The Paragon Press, 1993
© The Paragon Press and Hamish Fulton 2003

Untitled. Australia 1982
46·5 × 111. ACC45/1993

Mountain Skyline. Nepal 1983
86·5 × 99·3. ACC46/1993

SNOW LAKE LEAF STAR
TWIG HAWK CROW FISH
HOWL MIND MIST WALK
RAIN MOSS BEAR BONE
EYES WIND ROCK MOON
FROG DEER SEED CAMP
DAWN COLD DUST FIRE

SEVEN
WINDS
SEVEN
TWIGS
SEVEN
PATHS

Untitled. Alberta 1984
72 × 101·6 . ACC47/1993

Seven Winds. Scotland 1985
107 × 82·9. ACC48/1993

Untitled. Japan 1986
98·1 × 68·9. ACC49/1993

Untitled. Brittany 1987
47 × 110·7. ACC50/1993

Untitled. 21-Day Walk 1987
38·2 × 111·8. ACC51/1993

Fourteen Coast to Coast Walks. British Isles 1971–87
98·3 × 70 . ACC52/1993

Full Moon. Kent 1988
72 × 99 . ACC53/1993

Rock Fall Echo Dust. Baffin Island 1988
104·2 × 88 . ACC54/1993

NO THOUGHTS COUNTING SEVEN PACES ON SENJOH DAKE AT SUNSET

FACING MOUNT FUJI AND THE SECOND FULL MOON OF MAY 1988

A 19 DAY COAST TO COAST ROAD WALKING JOURNEY

TOYAMA BAY   ONTAKE SUMMIT   FUJI SUMMIT   SURUGA BAY

HONSHU JAPAN

No Thoughts Counting Seven Paces on Senjoh Dake at Sunset.
Japan 1988
60·4 × 101·7 . ACC55/1993

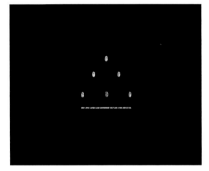

Twenty-One Walks Walking from One to Twenty-One Days.
Various Countries 1971–88
70·6 × 111·8 . ACC56/1993

Dead Dogs. Portugal and Spain 1989
80 × 111·8 . ACC57/1993

Untitled. Nepal 1989
78·7 × 95·8 . ACC58/1993

FURLONG, William b. 1944
Spoken For/Spoken About, 1998 (installation shot)
digital sound recording in 4 sections on 8-track hard disc and 8 speakers;
running time: 52 minutes, 15 seconds; purchased from the artist, 1999.
ACC38/1999

GABIE, Neville b. 1959
Kiln, 1986
wood and fired clay; 107 × 91·5 × 91·5; purchased from the artist, 1989.
ACC27/1989

GABO, Naum 1890–1977
Opus Eight, undated
monoprint; 30·2 × 23·8; gift of Nina Williams on the occasion of the
National Touring Exhibition from the South Bank Centre *Naum Gabo*, 1989.
ACC14/1989

GALLACCIO, Anya b. 1963
Couverture, 1994
chocolate, coconut butter, aluminium and printed paper;
20 × 17 × 17; purchased from Karsten Schubert, 1994.
ACC26/1994

GALLACCIO, Anya
(see also BUGS portfolio and SCREEN portfolio)

GALLACCIO, Anya b. 1963
Place a Candle, 1996 (installation shot)
printed glass, wood, wax and paper; 63 × 61 × 5; ed. 1/10; purchased from
Ridinghouse Editions, 1996. ACC1/1996

GASOI, Marvin b. 1949
Street Fair New York, 1983
cibachrome print, printed 1984; 27·9 × 35·7; purchased from the artist,
1988. ACC50/1990

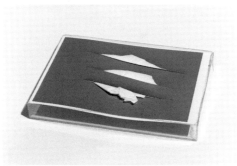

GENERAL IDEA (BRONSON, A. A. b. 1946; PARTZ, Felix
1945–94; ZONTAL, Jorge 1944–94)
Gesundheit – Why Not Sneeze, Lucio Fontana, 1991
card and paper; 10·8 × 15·2 × 1·9; unlimited edition; purchased from
Galerie A, 1994. ACC19/1997

GEORGE, Patrick b. 1923
Portrait of Joanna Drew, 1960–61
oil on canvas; 102 × 92; gift of Joanna Drew, 1992.
ACC16/1992

GHOSH, Amal b. 1933
Allegory III, 1987
acrylic on canvas; 127 × 153; purchased from the artist, 1989.
ACC28/1989

GILL, Alison b. 1966
Talking Dead, 1994
plaster, oil paint, synthetic and human hair, resin, polystyrene, plastic,
fabric and mixed media; 91 × 96 × 51; gift of Charles Saatchi, 1999.
ACC175/1998

GILLICK, Liam b. 1964
Who Controls the Near Future? Applied Complex Screen, 1999
(installation shot)
aluminium, steel and coloured perspex; 196·4 × 360·1 × 5·8; gift of the
artist; commissioned by the Hayward Gallery, 2000. ACC15/2002

GILLICK, Liam
(see also BOND, Henry and OTHER MEN'S FLOWERS portfolio)

GODFREY-ISAACS, Laura b. 1964
Plasticine Painting, 1995
plasticine on canvas; 35 × 35 × 10; purchased from the
Whitechapel Art Gallery, 1996. ACC4/1996

GODWIN, Fay b. 1931
Nightguard, Stonehenge (from Our Forbidden Land), 1988
gelatin silver print; 30·5 × 40·3; purchased from the artist, 1999.
ACC73/1999

GODWIN, Fay b. 1931
The Duke of Westminster's Estate, Forest of Bowland, 1988
gelatin silver print; 30·2 × 40·3; purchased from the artist, 1999.
ACC74/1999

GOLDEN, Pamela b. 1959
Mrs Watson, Signor Treci and Traldi at the Hospital, 1995
oil and encaustic on paper; 4·6 × 7; purchased from Gimpel Fils, 1997.
ACC43/1996

GOLDEN, Pamela b. 1959
Untitled (from the Mrs Watson Pours the Coffee series), 1995
oil and encaustic on paper; 4·4 × 7; purchased from Gimpel Fils, 1997.
ACC44/1996

GONTARSKI, Steven b. 1972
Arbeiter Samariter, 1997
PVC, synthetic hair, fabric and wadding; 101·6 × 122 × 71;
gift of Charles Saatchi, 2002. ACC29/2002

GONTARSKI, Steven b. 1972
Useless, 1997
PVC, polyester wadding, wood, synthetic clothing and transfer tattoo;
173 × 63 × 84; gift of Charles Saatchi, 2002. ACC30/2002

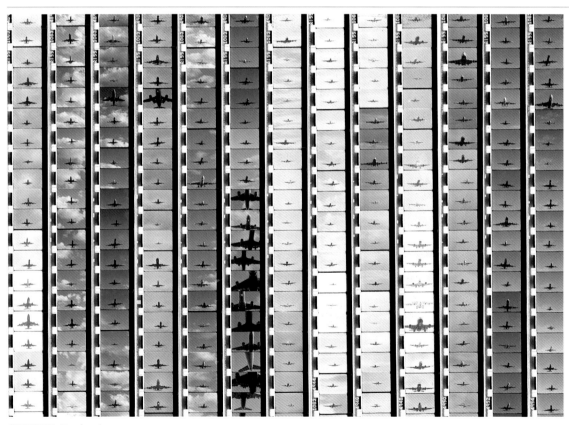

GOODWIN, Dryden b. 1971
One Thousand Nine Hundred and Ninety Eight, 1998 (still)
16mm film loop, 1,998 frames, projector; ed. 1/3; purchased from EC Art,
1998. ACC3/1998

GORDON, Douglas b. 1966
Painting No. 19: Mark Rothko / Betty Parsons, 1992
acrylic on canvas; 100 × 66; purchased from the artist, 1992.
ACC98/1991

GORDON, Douglas b. 1966
Croque Mort, 2000 (installation shot)
c-type photographic print; 7 works, each 95 × 135 or 135 × 95; ed. 4/13;
purchased from Lisson Gallery, 2001.
ACC38–44/2000 and ACC70/2000

GORMLEY, Antony b. 1950
Bearing Light, 1990*

woodblock prints; 12 works, each 57 × 29·5 or 29·5 × 57; all artist's proofs
from an ed. of 30; purchased from Frith Street Gallery, 1993. ACC1/1993 and
ACC34–44/1993

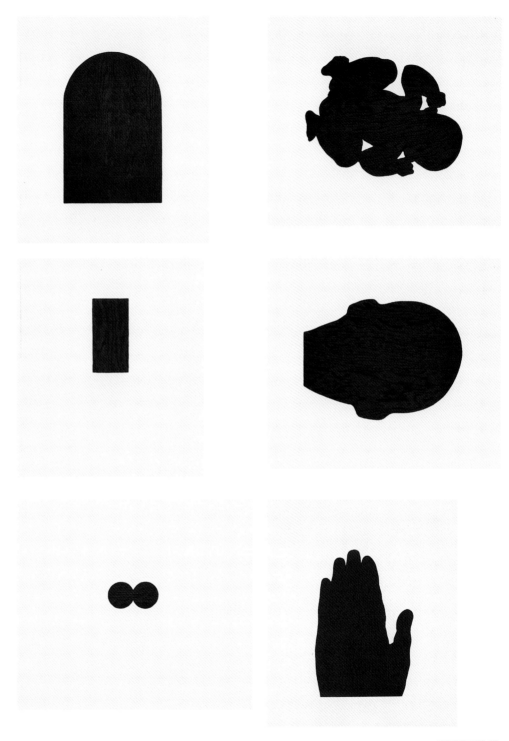

GORMLEY, Antony b. 1950
Field for the British Isles, 1993 (detail)
terracotta; dimensions variable, between 3,000 and 6,000 square feet;
purchased from White Cube with the assistance of The Henry Moore
Foundation and the National Art Collections Fund, 1995. ACC10/1995

GRAHAM, Dan b. 1942
One, 1992
plastic; 7·5 × 9·2 × 0·8; unnumbered edition of 500; purchased from
Yves Geraert, 1994. ACC20/1997

GRAHAM, Paul b. 1956
Untitled No. 11, 1999
Fujiflex archive print, printed 2001; 75·6 × 99·5; ed. 3/6; purchased
from Anthony Reynolds Gallery, 2001. ACC29/2000

GRAHAM, Paul b. 1956
Untitled No. 12, 1999
Fujiflex archive print, printed 2001; 75·6 × 99·5; ed. 2/6; purchased
from Anthony Reynolds Gallery, 2001. ACC30/2000

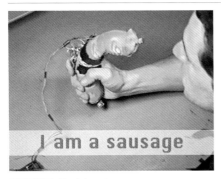

GRANJON, Paul b. 1965
2 Minutes of Experimentation and Entertainment, 1996–98
(still from Episode #2, the Cybernetic Parrot Sausage)
VHS video tape, 7 episodes; running time: 3 minutes each episode;
ed. 1/5; purchased from the artist, 2002. ACC12/2002

GRANJON, Paul b. 1965
CCTV Soundscape, 2001
model landscape, perspex, aluminium, motors, computers, video camera and
sound system; 120 × 140 × 140; ed. 1/2; purchased from the artist, 2002.
Commissioned by Lovebytes (www.lovebytes.org.uk) with support from the
Arts Council of Wales. ACC13/2002

GRANSDEN, Frances 1967–94
Untitled (8), 1992 (1 of 2 works)
black-and-white photograph; 2 works, each 50·8 × 40·6;
donated from the exhibition *Image '90s*, 1992.
ACC61–62/1993

GRASSIE, Andrew b. 1966
Edwards Airforce Base 1,2,3, 1998 (detail)
oil on board; 3 parts, each 20·5 × 28·5; purchased from Mobile Home, 2000.
ACC61/1999

GRASSIE, Andrew b. 1966
Pleiadian Space Craft, 2000
metal; 6 diameter; purchased from Mobile Home, 2000.
ACC69/1999

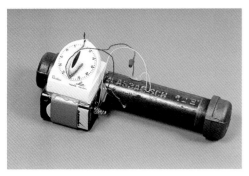

GREEN, Gregory b. 1959
Pipe Bomb #3 (LA), 1993
metal, plastic, glue, wire and paint; 34·3 × 10· 2 × 14·6;
gift of Charles Saatchi, 2002. ACC31/2002

GREEN, Gregory b. 1959
Work Station No. 5 (London 1996), 1994
mixed media; dimensions variable; gift of Charles Saatchi, 2002.
ACC32/2002

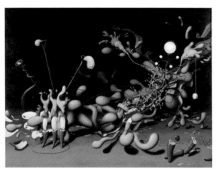

GREENWOOD, John b. 1959
Enjoy Yourself, 1991
oil on canvas; 138 × 183; gift of Charles Saatchi, 1999.
ACC177/1998

GREENWOOD, John b. 1959
How Many Doughnuts Have You Collected?, 1992
oil on canvas; 138 × 183; gift of Charles Saatchi, 1999.
ACC176/1998

GREGORY, Joy b. 1959
Elegance, 1999–2000
unique photograph with salt and sun processing; 75·5 × 55;
purchased from Zelda Cheatle Gallery, 2001. ACC58/2000

GREGORY, Joy b. 1959
Leather Bag, 1999–2000
unique photograph with salt and sun processing; 75·5 × 55;
purchased from Zelda Cheatle Gallery, 2001. ACC57/2000

GREGORY, Joy b. 1959
String Bag, 1999–2000
unique photograph with salt and sun processing; 75·5 × 55;
purchased from Zelda Cheatle Gallery, 2001. ACC59/2000

GRIERSON, Robin Lewis b. 1962
Dublin, Eire, 1992 (1 of 2 works)
silver bromide print; 2 works, each 54·5 × 35·5;
donated from the exhibition *Image '90s*, 1992. ACC63–64/1993

GRIERSON, Robin Lewis b. 1962
Miner Coming off Shift, Harworth, Nottinghamshire, 1992
silver bromide print; 35·5 × 54·5; purchased from Flowers East, 1993.
ACC32/1993

GRIFFITHS, Brian b. 1968
Untitled, Osaka, Taylon and Ron, 1998
mixed media; dimensions variable; gift of Charles Saatchi, 2002.
ACC33/2002

GRIFFITHS, David b. 1961
I Spy Stranger, 1994 (detail)
black-and-white photograph; 1–5 from the series *I Spy Stranger*, each
45·5 × 55·5; purchased from the artist, 1995. ACC117/1995

GUNNING, Lucy b. 1964
Climbing Around My Room, 1993 (still)
Betacam sp video tape; running time: 7 minutes, 30 seconds;
purchased from the artist, 1995. ACC22/1995

GUNNING, Lucy b. 1964
The Horse Impressionists, 1994 (still)
VHS video tape; running time: 7 minutes, 30 seconds; ed. 2/8;
purchased from the artist, 1995. ACC23/1995

GUSSIN, Graham b. 1960
Airline No.2, 1990
black-and-white photograph and LEDs; 117 × 178; gift of Charles Saatchi, 1999. ACC178/1998

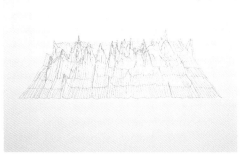

GUSSIN, Graham b. 1960
Porno Landscape (We wish that you could be here with us), 1996
pencil on paper; 63.3 × 89.1; purchased from Lotta Hammer, 1997. ACC17/1996

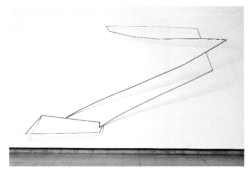

HALL, Nigel b. 1943
Four Figure Sum, 1976
painted aluminium; 201 × 373.3 × 102; gift of Arnolfini Collection Trust, 2001. ACC68/2000

HALL, Victoria b. 1972
Family Tree 1, 1995 (detail)
fishing line on lith film; 81 × 401; purchased from Norwich Gallery, 1995. ACC17/1995

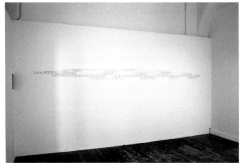

HALL, Victoria b. 1972
Family Tree 2, 1995 (installation shot)
Letraset line on adhesive acetate; 46 × 376; purchased from Norwich Gallery, 1995. ACC17/1995

HAMILTON, Richard b. 1922
Portrait of Derek Jarman, 1996–97
colour pigment transfer print; 39.4 × 39.4; ed. 30/40; purchased from Richard Salmon Gallery for the Elton John AIDS Foundation, 1997. ACC3/1997

HANNEY, Sonya
(see DADE, Adam)

HAPASKA, Siobhán b. 1963
Far, 1995
fibreglass, opalescent paint and acrylic lacquer; 122 × 244 × 76; gift of Charles Saatchi, 2002. ACC34/2002

HAPASKA, Siobhán b. 1963
Saint Christopher, 1995
wax, hair, cotton and oil paint; 90 × 50 × 70; gift of Charles Saatchi, 1999. ACC179/1998

HAPASKA, Siobhán b. 1963
Heart, 1995
Indian rosewood veneer, MDF, audio components (sound); 76 × 291 × 18·5;
purchased from Entwistle, 1997. ACC57/1997

HAPASKA, Siobhán
(see also SCREEN portfolio)

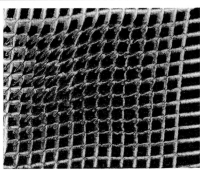

HARDING, Alexis b. 1973
Untitled (Study), 1995
oil and gloss on canvas; 61 × 76·2; purchased from Martin Maloney, 1996.
ACC24/1995

HAROLD, Jim b. 1948
Four Appearances (Newton, Marat, Coleridge and Burke), 1995
(detail)
silver bromide print mounted on aluminium; 4 parts, each 61 × 61;
purchased from the artist, 1997. ACC49/1996

HARRIS, Jane b. 1956
Aureole, 1992–94
oil on canvas; 137 × 213; purchased from Anderson O'Day Gallery, 1995.
ACC111/1995

HARRIS, Jane b. 1956
Untitled Drawing 3, 1998–99
pencil on paper; 55.5 × 76; purchased from Anderson O'Day Gallery, 1999.
ACC4/1999

HARRIS, Jane b. 1956
Untitled Drawing 22, 1999
pencil on paper; 56 × 76; purchased from Anderson O'Day Gallery, 1999.
ACC27/1999

HARRISON, Paul
(see WOOD, John)

HARTLEY, Alex b. 1963
Untitled (after Monet), 1991
colour photograph, MDF, aluminium and glass; 57 × 244 × 15;
purchased from Anderson O'Day Gallery, 1991.   ACC69/1991

HARTLEY, Alex b. 1963
Untitled (Miro), 1992
satin acid-etched glass, MDF and photograph; 60 × 85 × 11;
gift of Charles Saatchi, 1999. ACC180/1998

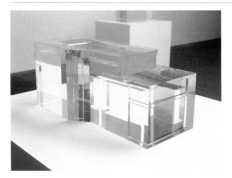

HARTLEY, Alex b. 1963
Untitled, 1995
wood, acrylic and photograph; 27 × 60 × 30, plinth 85 × 120 × 85;
gift of Charles Saatchi, 2002. ACC35/2002

HATOUM, Mona b. 1952
Measures of Distance, 1988 (still)
Betacam sp video tape; running time: 15 minutes, 26 seconds;
purchased from the artist, 1999. ACC14/1999

HATOUM, Mona b. 1952
The Light at the End, 1989 (installation shot)
iron, steel, brass, glass, aluminium and electric elements;
frame 165 × 112·5 × 5, installation dimensions variable;
purchased from the artist, 1990. ACC2/1990

HATOUM, Mona b. 1952
+ and -, 1994
wood, metal and sand (kinetic); 8 × 30 × 30; ed. 2/4;
purchased from the artist, 1994. ACC44/1997

HATOUM, Mona b. 1952
Plotting Table, 1998
wood, MDF, UV lights and fluorescent paint; 262.5 × 144 × 81; ed. 2/3;
purchased from White Cube, 1999. ACC49/1999

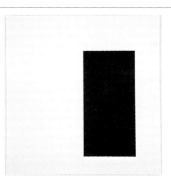

HATT, Christine b. 1954
Outside Inside, 1991
wax crayon and graphite on paper; 122 × 122;
purchased from Annely Juda Fine Art, 1992. ACC4/1992

HATT, Christine b. 1954
There not There, 1991
wax crayon and graphite on paper; 122 × 122;
purchased from Annely Juda Fine Art, 1992. ACC5/1992

HAYS, Dan b. 1966
Guinea Pig, 1995
oil on canvas; 16 × 22; purchased from Studio and Education Access, 1995.
ACC39/1995

HAYS, Dan b. 1966
Guinea Pig, 1995
oil on canvas; 16 × 22; purchased from Studio and Education Access, 1995.
ACC91/1995

HAYS, Dan b. 1966
Guinea Pig, 1995
oil on canvas; 16 × 22; purchased from Studio and Education Access, 1995.
ACC92/1995

HAYS, Dan b. 1966
Guinea Pig, 1995
oil on canvas; 16 × 22; purchased from Studio and Education Access, 1995.
ACC93/1995

HAYS, Dan b. 1966
Guinea Pig, 1995
oil on canvas; 16 × 22; gift of the artist, 1995.
ACC94/1995

HEAD, Tim b. 1946
Exquisite Corpse 2, 1995
black-and-white photograph; 54 × 81; purchased from Frith Street Gallery, 1995. ACC26/1995

HEAD, Tim b. 1946
Exquisite Corpse 4, 1995
black-and-white photograph; 54 × 81; purchased from Frith Street Gallery, 1995. ACC27/1995

HEATH, Claude b. 1964
Tender Ground No.1, 1996
chalk, oil-based paint and acrylic on canvas; 383.5 × 317.5; gift of Charles Saatchi, 1999. ACC181/1998

HEATH, Claude b. 1964
Tender Ground No.2, 1996
chalk, oil-based paint and acrylic on canvas; 383.5 × 317.5; gift of Charles Saatchi, 1999. ACC182/1998

HEATH, Claude b. 1964
Tender Ground No.3, 1996
chalk, oil-based paint and acrylic on canvas; 383.5 × 317.5; gift of Charles Saatchi, 1999. ACC183/1998

HEATH, Claude b. 1964
Tender Ground No.4, 1996
chalk, oil-based paint and acrylic on canvas; 383 × 317.5; gift of Charles Saatchi, 1999. ACC184/1998

HEMSWORTH, Gerard b. 1945
Kiss my Arse, 1994
acrylic on canvas; 214 × 244; purchased from Anthony Reynolds Gallery,
1995. ACC95/1995

HENOCQ, Ron b. 1950
Boll, 1996 (1 of 4 works)
linoprint; 4 works, each approx· 200 × 140; artist's proof from an edition of
20; purchased from Snow Gallery, 2001. ACC30–33/2001

HERMAN, Andrew
(see OTHER MEN'S FLOWERS portfolio)

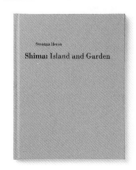

HERON, Susanna b. 1949
Shima: Island and Garden, 1987–92
book; 21·5 × 17 × 1; ed. 6/25; purchased from the artist, 1993.
ACC10/1992

HERON, Susanna b. 1949
Pine V (split vertical), 1990 (1 of 12 works)
cibachrome photograph; 12 works, each 41·3 × 30·5 or 30·5 × 41·3;
unnumbered edition of 10; purchased from the artist, 1993.
ACC28/1993 from a series ACC19/1993 and ACC21–31/1993

HILLER, Susan b. 1942
The Secrets of Sunset Beach, 1988 (detail)
c-type photograph; 10 parts, each 72·4 × 53·8 or 53·8 × 72·4; purchased from
the artist, 1989. ACC44/1989

HILLER, Susan b. 1942
Wild Talents, 1997 (installation shot)
2 video disks and 1 Betacam sp video tape and VHS video tape, light bulbs,
wood and television monitor; running time: 60 minutes, installation
dimensions variable; ed. 1/3; purchased from Wigmore Fine Art, 1998.
ACC10/1998

HIRST, Damien b. 1965
Relationships, 1991
glass, plastic and paper; 14·5 × 6·2 diameter;
unnumbered edition of 100; purchased from White Cube, 1994.
ACC21/1997

HIRST, Damien
(see also LONDON portfolio)

HIRST, Damien b. 1965
He Tried to Internalise Everything, 1992–94
glass, steel, foam, rubber, vinyl, wood and plastic; 213 × 213 × 305;
purchased from White Cube, with assistance from The Henry Moore
Foundation, 1996. ACC21/1995

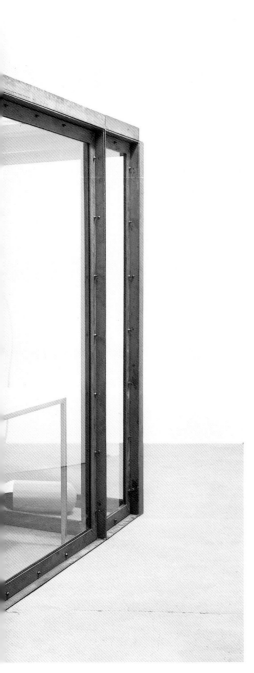

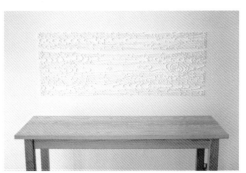

HIRST, Nicky b. 1963
Wall 1, 1993
wood, plastic and metal; 75 × 152·3 × 55·7; gift of Charles Saatchi, 1999.
ACC185/1998

HOLZER, Jenny b. 1950
Untitled, 1991
rubber, wood and ink; 10 × 15 × 10; unlimited edition;
purchased from Workfortheeyetodo, 1994. ACC22/1997

HOOKER, Charlie b. 1953
Wave-Wall 2, 1991 (installation shot)
pastel, chalk, motorized pendulums and sound (kinetic); 650 × 3000 × 150;
purchased from the artist, 1992. ACC90/1991

HOPKINS, Louise b. 1965
Aurora 13, 1995–96
oil paint on reverse of furnishing fabric; 183 × 130;
gift of Charles Saatchi, 1999. ACC186/1998

HOPKINS, Louise b. 1965
Songsheet 4, 1996
gouache on paper; 30·4 × 45·7; purchased from Andrew Mummery, 1997.
ACC15/1996

HOSKING, Mark b. 1972
Untitled (Lowland Rice), 1998
steel; 2 parts: 163 × 117 × 190 and 104 × 68 × 284;
gift of Charles Saatchi, 2002. ACC36/2002

HOUSHIARY, Shirazeh b. 1955
Cube of Man, 1992
lead, gold leaf and wood; 283 × 65 × 65; purchased from Lisson Gallery,
1996. ACC57/1995

HUBBARD, John b. 1931
Palms Against the Light, Tresco, 1986
chalk on paper; 56·5 × 76·2; purchased from the artist, 1990.
ACC45/1990

HUBBARD, John b. 1931
Twisting, Gripping, (Tree Trunks), 1986
chalk on paper; 71 × 56; purchased from the artist, 1990.
ACC46/1990

HUGHES, Dean b. 1974
Two Pieces of Ruled A4 Paper, 1997
lithoprint on paper; print 29·7 × 21, paper 34 × 47; purchased from the artist, 2000. ACC63/1999

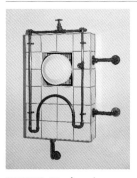

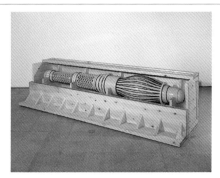

HUGHES, Stephen b. 1957
Extractor, 1988
ceramic, wood, copper, steel, plastic and resin;
120 × 80 × 38; purchased from the artist, 1991.
ACC29/1991

HUGHES, Stephen b. 1957
Container One, 1991
polyethylene, plastic and wood; 75 × 58 × 308;
purchased from the artist, 1991. ACC44/1991

HUGONIN, James b. 1950
Untitled, 1988–89
oil and wax on plywood; 170·2 × 152·4;
purchased from the artist, 1989. ACC23/1989

HUME, Gary b. 1962
*Frankfürter Allgemeine, Le monde, The Independent,
International Herald Tribune*, 1991
printed paper and card; 3 parts 4 × 45 × 33, 1 part 4 × 36 × 26; ed. of 25;
purchased from G-W Press, 1994. ACC23/1997

HUME, Gary b. 1962
Moonbeam Rising, 1994
gloss, egg-shell and satin paint on board; 244·4 × 122·5;
purchased from the artist, 1994. ACC21/1994

HUME, Gary b. 1962
Four Feet in the Garden, 1995
gloss paint on aluminium; 221 × 170·9; purchased from White Cube, 1995.
ACC3/1995

HUME, Gary
(see also OTHER MEN'S FLOWERS portfolio)

HUSSAIN, Kabir b. 1960
Sullstani, 1988
bronze; 15·2 × 4·5 × 0·5; ed. 1/5;
purchased from the artist, 1989. ACC35/1989

IMPEY, Sax b. 1969
Lottery, 2000
paper, oil and undercoat on panel; 5 parts, total 66 × 345;
purchased from the artist, 2001. ACC4/2001

INNES, Callum b. 1962
Two Identified Forms, 1991
oil on canvas; 164·7 × 149·7; purchased from
Frith Street Gallery, 1992. ACC84/1991

IRVINE, Jaki b. 1966
Star, 1994 (still)
black-and-white Super-8 film with sound; running time: 3 minutes; ed. 2/3;
purchased from Frith Street Gallery, 1997. ACC2/1997

ISAACS, John b. 1968
Say it isn't so, 1994
mixed media; 204 × 129 × 132; gift of Charles Saatchi, 2002.
ACC37/2002

ISAACS, John b. 1968
Untitled (Dodo), 1994
fibreglass, silicone rubber, electric mechanism, glass and acrylic;
81 × 72 × 41; gift of Charles Saatchi, 2002. ACC38/2002

ISAACS, John b. 1968
Untitled (Monkey), 1995
wax, hair, glass, metal and plastic; 50 × 40 × 30;
gift of Charles Saatchi, 1999. ACC187/1998

ISAACS, John b. 1968
Untitled (The Beast With a Million Eyes), 1995
vinyl, speakers, flex and wood (sound); 120 × 90 × 110;
gift of Charles Saatchi, 1999. ACC188/1998

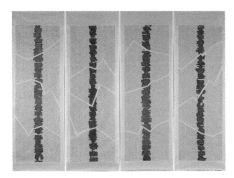

JACOBS, Sarah b.1944
In Blessing, 1991–92 (4 of 7 parts)
ink on gampi paper; 7 parts, each 290.5 × 97.5; purchased from the artist, 2000. ACC42/1999

JANTJES, Gavin b.1948
Freedom Hunters, 1977
screenprint with collage; 70 × 100; purchased from Edward Totah Gallery, 1991. ACC30/1990

JANTJES, Gavin b.1948
No More, 1977
screenprint with collage; 100 × 70; purchased from Edward Totah Gallery, 1991. ACC31/1990

JANTJES, Gavin b.1948
A South African Colouring Book, 1989 * (1 of 11 works)
screenprint and collage; 11 works, each 60 × 45; purchased from Edward Totah Gallery, 1991. ACC32–42/1990

JANTJES, Gavin b.1948
Untitled, 1989
sand, tissue paper and acrylic on canvas; 200 × 300 × 3; purchased from Edward Totah Gallery, 1991. ACC29/1990

JARAY, Tess b. 1937
Terrace, 1991
etching; image 20·2 × 39·3, paper 38·5 × 57; ed. 20/20; purchased from the artist, 1998. ACC12/1998

JARAY, Tess b. 1937
At Regensburg he crossed... (from the *From the Rings of Saturn and Vertigo* series), 2001 (detail)
screenprint; 2 parts: image 62 × 43·5, paper 85 × 64, text sheet 61 × 44; ed. 17/44; purchased from Purdy Hicks Gallery, 2001. ACC34/2001

JARAY, Tess b. 1937
I was watching... (from the *From the Rings of Saturn and Vertigo* series), 2001 (detail)
screenprint; 2 parts: image 73 × 97·5, paper 80 × 120, text sheet 74 × 50; ed. 17/44; purchased from Purdy Hicks Gallery, 2001. ACC35/2001

JARMAN, Derek 1942–94
Morphine, 1992
oil on photocopy on canvas; 251·5 × 179; purchased from Karsten Schubert, 1993. ACC11/1992

JOFFE, Chantal b. 1969
Untitled (nos.1–6), 1995–96
oil on gesso on board; 6 works, each 28 × 21·5; gift of Charles Saatchi, 1999. ACC189–194/1998

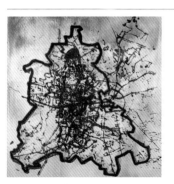

JOHNSON, Glenys b. 1952
Berlin, 1989
pigment and photo-emulsion on canvas; 233·5 × 231·2; purchased from the artist, 1994. ACC19/1994

JOHNSON, Nerys 1942–2001
Double-page study: Iris, tulip and 'cat's paw' stem with magenta ground, 1995
watercolour and gouache on paper; 30 × 42; purchased from Woodlands Art Gallery, 1995. ACC19/1995. © Nerys Johnson Estate 2003

JOHNSON, Nerys 1942–2001
Iris with deep pink anenome, rosehip and viridian leaf, 1999
gouache on paper; 14 × 9.5; purchased from Nerys Johnson Contemporary Art Fund, 2001. ACC52/2001. © Nerys Johnson Estate 2003

JOHNSON, Nerys 1942–2001
Nasturtium, iris bud and rosehip with cobalt leaf (crimson stem), 1999
gouache on paper; 18.5 × 12.5; purchased from Nerys Johnson Contemporary Art Fund, 2001. ACC53/2001. © Nerys Johnson Estate 2003

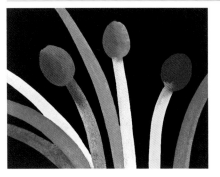

JOHNSON, Nerys 1942–2001
Three purple tulips with multi-leaf spray III, 2000
gouache on paper; 16 × 21; purchased from Nerys Johnson Contemporary Art Fund, 2001. ACC55/2001. © Nerys Johnson Estate 2003

JOHNSON, Nerys 1942–2001
White and purple gladioli with blue leaf, 2000
gouache on paper; 28 × 15; purchased from Nerys Johnson Contemporary Art Fund, 2001. ACC54/2001. © Nerys Johnson Estate 2003

JOHNSON, Steve b. 1953
Binoculars (charm no.9), 1995
bronze; 9.2 × 25.3 × 21.3; purchased from the artist, 1995.
ACC20/1995

JOHNSTON, Alan b. 1945
Untitled, 1985
pencil on canvas; 250 × 200; purchased from Arnolfini Gallery, 1989.
ACC41/1989

JONES, Sarah b. 1959
Actor, 1995
c-type print on aluminium; 152 × 152;
purchased from the artist, 1995. ACC35/1995

JONES, Sarah b. 1959
Consulting Room, 1995
c-type print on aluminium; 152 × 152;
purchased from the artist, 1995. ACC36/1995

JONES, Zebedee b. 1970
Blue/Green, 1993
oil and wax on canvas; 101 × 66·5;
purchased from the artist, 1994. ACC23/1994

JOSEPH, Peter b. 1929
Bright Orange with Green, 1988
acrylic on canvas; 151 × 137; purchased from
Lisson Gallery, 1993. ACC8/1992

JOYCE, Paul b. 1941
Blue Gum Eucalyptus Globulus, the Long Walk, Tresco, 1989
silver print; 50·2 × 38·9; purchased from the artist, 1991. ACC24/1991

JOYCE, Paul b. 1941
Cypress and Succulents, the Cypress Rockery, Tresco, 1989
silver print; 50·2 × 38·9; purchased from the artist, 1991. ACC25/1991

JOYCE, Paul b. 1941
In the Woods, Abbotsbury, 1989
silver print; 50·2 × 38·9; purchased from the artist, 1991.
ACC23/1991

JOYCE, Paul b. 1941
Metrosideros Tomentosa, the Lighthouse Walk, Tresco, 1989
silver print; 38·9 × 50·2; purchased from the artist, 1991. ACC22/1991

JOYCE, Paul b. 1941
Palm Tree Bole, Tresco, 1989
silver print; 38·9 × 50·2; purchased from the artist, 1991. ACC26/1991

JULIEN, Isaac b. 1960
The Long Road to Mazatlan, 1999 (still)
Collaboration: Isaac Julien and Javier de Frutos. Director: Isaac Julien.
Choreography and movement: Javier de Frutos; video projection on DVD,
video disc and Betacam sp video tape; running time: 20 minutes; ed. 2/4;
purchased from Victoria Miro Gallery, 2001. ACC1/2002

KABAKOV, Ilya b. 1933
Two Friends, 1992
screenprint on card, plastic and paper; 5 × 11·5 × 14·5;
ed. 31/50; purchased from Parkett, 1997. ACC24/1997

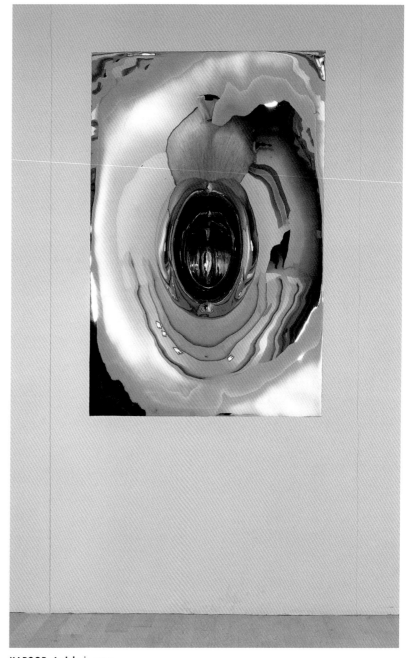

KAPOOR, Anish b. 1954
Untitled, 1997–98 (installation shot)
stainless steel; 140 × 92·6 × 100, weight 272 kg; ed. 2/3; purchased from
Lisson Gallery with assistance from The Henry Moore Foundation, 1997.
ACC63/1996

KARSHAN, Linda b. 1947
8.6.00, 2000
graphite on paper; 76 × 56;
purchased from Dee Glasoe Gallery, 2001.
ACC56/2000

KARSHAN, Linda b. 1947
15.6.00, 2000
graphite on paper; 76 × 56;
purchased from Dee Glasoe Gallery, 2001.
ACC54/2000

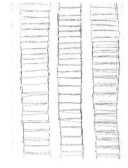

KARSHAN, Linda b. 1947
5.8.00, 2000
graphite on paper; 76 × 56;
purchased from Dee Glasoe Gallery, 2001.
ACC55/2000

KAUR, Permindar b. 1965
Innocence, 1993
cotton and iron; 60 × 72; purchased from the artist, 1996.
ACC59/1995

KAY, Emma b. 1961
The World from Memory no.3, 1999
pencil on paper; 145 × 242; purchased from The Approach, 2000.
ACC1/2000

KAYLEY, Ali b. 1969
Poor Cow, 1994
plastic; 89·2 × 25·1; unlimited edition;
purchased from Sarah Staton, 1994. ACC25/1997

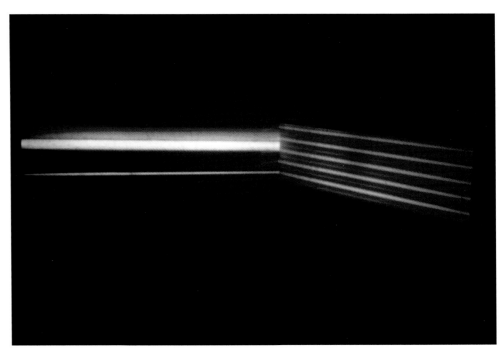

KEANE, Tina b. 1949
Transposition, 1995 (installation shot)
Betacam sp video tape projection on 2 screens; running time: 20 minutes;
ed. 1/3; purchased from the artist, 1998. ACC23/1998

KEARSEY, Mike b. 1942
Seascape, 1984
resin, aluminium powder and glass fibre; 39·7 × 47 × 2·9;
purchased from the artist, 1989. ACC36/1989

KEMPLEN, Tony b. 1959
SK329858 1944–94, 1994
offset lithograph on card and paper; 55 parts, each 8·8 × 5·8; ed. 8/100;
purchased from the artist, 1995. ACC1/1995

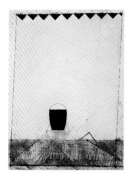

KENNY, Michael 1941–99
Instruments of Passion II, 1982
charcoal, ink and acrylic on paper; 101·5 × 76·5;
purchased from the artist, 1999. ACC39/1998

KENNY, Michael 1941–99
Instruments of Passion IV, 1982
charcoal, ink and acrylic on paper; 101·5 × 76·5;
purchased from the artist, 1999. ACC40/1998

KEY, Joan b. 1948
BOO (II), 1994
oil on canvas; 137 × 305; purchased from Richard Salmon Gallery, 1996.
ACC5/1996

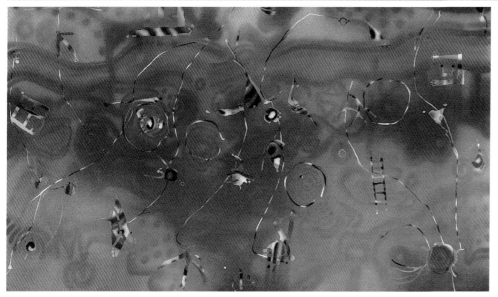

KHANNA, Balraj b. 1940
Coming from Rajasthan, 1984
acrylic on canvas; 168 × 304; purchased from the artist, 1989.
ACC28/1990

KHANNA, Balraj b. 1940
Apple Green, 1991
acrylic on canvas; 114 × 114; purchased from the artist, 1991.
ACC38/1991

KILLIP, Chris b. 1946
Rocker and Rosie Going Home, 1982
silver bromide print; 62 × 70; purchased from the artist, 1989.
ACC53/1989

KIRK, Joanna b. 1963
Michael and Margaret, 1994 *
pastel on paper; 2 works, each 241 × 149; gift of Charles Saatchi, 1999.
ACC195–196/1988

KIRK, Joanna b. 1963
Jacqui and Katharine, 1995
pastel on paper; 218·5 × 148·5; purchased from Todd Gallery, 1997.
ACC35/1996

KIRTI b. 1953
Damsel, 1989
wood; 147 × 28 × 20; purchased from the artist, 1991.
ACC33/1991

after **KLEIN, Yves** 1928–62
Untitled, 1991
sponge, plastic; 5·5 × 5·5 × 5·5; unlimited edition; purchased from XX
Multiples, 1994. ACC26/1997

KOUNELLIS, Jannis b. 1936
Le vin du musée, 1986
glass and paper; 30·1 height, 7·6 diameter; edition of 1000;
purchased from Harry Ruhé, 1994. ACC27/1997

KOVATS, Tania b. 1966
Virgin in a Condom, 1990
resin, rubber, paint and wood; 11 × 3 × 3; ed. 4/12;
purchased from Laure Genillard Gallery, 1994. ACC28/1997

KOVATS, Tania b. 1966
Grotto, 1995
fibreglass, paint, wax, varnish, moss, silk, MDF, wood and perfume; 230 ×
200 × 150; purchased from Laure Genillard Gallery, 1995. ACC7/1995

KOWALSKY, Elaine b. 1948
Screen Kiss, 1989
wood and lino cut; 76·5 × 56; ed. 4/10;
purchased from the artist, 1993. ACC110/1997

KOZLOFF, Max b. 1933
Luna Park, Liège, 1986
c-type print; 32 × 47·5; purchased from the artist, 1988. ACC55/1990

KRENKERS, Brigitte
(see DAHN, Walter)

KUDRYASHOV, Oleg b. 1932
Construction Plate N.1804 (N.1805 & N.1806), 1989
drypoint and watercolour; 70·7 × 63·5 × 26·7; purchased from Francis
Graham-Dixon Gallery, 1991. ACC37/1991

LAGO, Darren b. 1965
Ferrari Snow, 1996
plastic and paint; 16 × 26 × 9; gift of Charles Saatchi, 1999.
ACC197/1998

LAGO, Darren b. 1965
This is Not a Pipe, 1996
plastic, briar wood and flex; 13·5 × 25 × 6; gift of Charles Saatchi, 1999.
ACC198/1998

LALIC, Maria b. 1952
Lead Fall – Chrome Yellow, 1991
oil paint, linen, lead and wood; 210 × 30 × 7; purchased from Todd Gallery,
1991. ACC71/1991

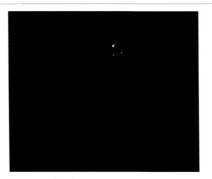

LAMBIE, Jim b. 1964
Ultralow, 1998 (still)
Betacam sp; running time: 15 minutes; ed. 2/10; purchased from
The Modern Institute, 2000. ACC43/1999

LAMBIE, Jim b. 1964
Sid Vicious, 2001
printed poster on foamboard with black glitter; 43 × 60 × 20 ;
purchased from Sadie Coles HQ, 2001. ACC3/2001

LANDEN, Clive b. 1950
Mustelid (A48), 1994
chromogenic print; 39 × 31; purchased from the artist, 2000.
ACC59/1999

LANDEN, Clive b. 1950
phasianus colchicus (A38), 1994
chromogenic print; 39 × 31; purchased from the artist, 2000.
ACC58/1999

LANDY, Michael
(see also LONDON portfolio)

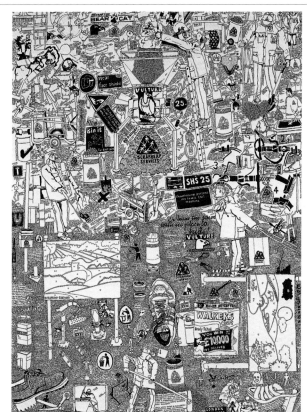

LANDY, Michael b. 1963
Scrapheap Services, 1995
ink on paper; 76 × 56; purchased from Karsten Schubert, 1995.
ACC44/1995

LANDY, Michael b. 1963
We Leave the Scum with No Place to Hide, 1995
aluminium, ink, wood and perspex; 94 × 19 × 19; ed. 1/6; purchased from
Ridinghouse Editions, 1995. ACC8/1995

LANE, Abigail b. 1967
Houses and Occupants No. 1, 1991
photograph and glass; 39 × 49·5 × 1·5; gift of Charles Saatchi, 1999.
ACC199/1998

LANE, Abigail b. 1967
Houses and Occupants No. 2, 1991
photograph and glass; 39 × 49·5 × 1·5; gift of Charles Saatchi, 1999.
ACC200/1998

LANE, Abigail b. 1967
Houses and Occupants No.3, 1991
glass and photograph; 49·5 × 39 × 1·5;
purchased from Anderson O'Day Gallery, 1991. ACC68/1991

LANE, Abigail
(see also SCREEN portfolio)

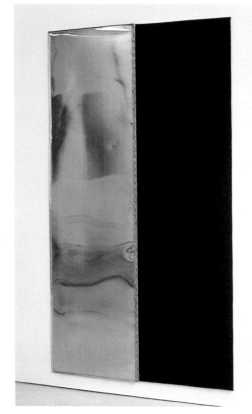

LANG, Liane b. 1973
Licking II, 1999 (still)
Betacam sp video; running time: 5 minutes, 27 seconds; ed. 1/4;
purchased from Jenny Todd Gallery, 2000. ACC65/1999

LANE, Abigail b. 1967
Ink Pad 1, 1991
aluminium, MDF, cotton, felt and ink; 168 × 92 × 1·5;
gift of Charles Saatchi, 1999. ACC201/1998

LANGLANDS & BELL
(**LANGLANDS, Ben** b.1955 and **BELL, Nikki** b.1959)
Rank Xerox, Düsseldorf, 1990
wood, paint, lacquer and glass; 90 × 90 × 15; gift of Charles Saatchi, 1999.
ACC203/1998

LANGLANDS & BELL
(**LANGLANDS, Ben** b.1955 and **BELL, Nikki** b.1959)
D.G. Bank, Frankfurt, 1992
wood, paint, lacquer and glass; 90 × 90 × 15; gift of Charles Saatchi, 1999.
ACC202/1998

LANGLANDS & BELL
(see also LONDON portfolio)

LANSLEY, Jo b. 1964 and **BENDON, Helen** b.1974
The Sweet Smell of Success, 1997 (still)
Betacam sp video tape; projection size 180 × 240;
running time: 2 minutes; ed. 1/3; purchased from the artists, 2000.
ACC39/1999

LAWSON, Thomas b. 1951
Christminster, 1984
oil on canvas; 183·5 × 366·6; purchased from Anthony Reynolds Gallery,
1991. ACC43/1990

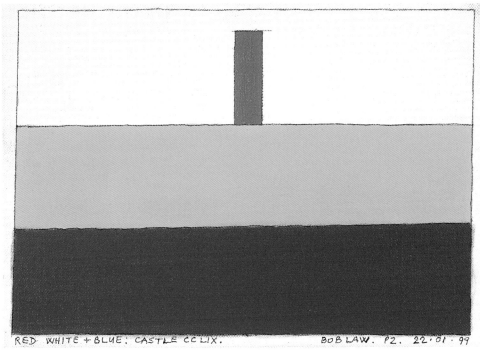

LAW, Bob b. 1934
Red, White + Blue Castle CCLIX PZ 22.01.99, 1999
oil and pencil on linen; 26 × 36; purchased from Marlene Eleini Gallery, 1999.
ACC29/1999

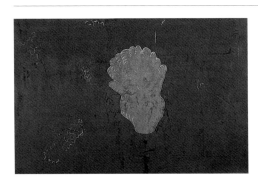

LEAPMAN, David b. 1959
Past Behaviour, 1990
acrylic on canvas; 117·8 × 180·2; purchased from Todd Gallery, 1990.
ACC6/1990

LEAPMAN, David b. 1959
Pilot Schemer, 1992
acrylic and interference acrylic on canvas; 166 × 216;
gift of Charles Saatchi, 1999. ACC205/1998

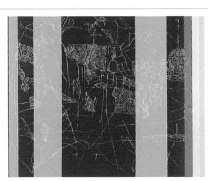

LEAPMAN, David b. 1959
Slowburn Escort, 1992
day-glo acrylic and interference acrylic on canvas; 171 × 215;
gift of Charles Saatchi, 1999. ACC204/1998

LEAPMAN, Edwina b. 1931
Tall, Very Dark Blue, 1991
acrylic on canvas; 218·5 × 163·1; purchased from
Annely Juda Fine Art, 1991. ACC70/1991

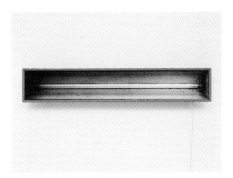

LEWANDOWSKA, Marysia b. 1955
Strip Light, 1991
black-and-white transparency, painted wooden box and fluorescent light;
30 × 167 × 20; gift of Charles Saatchi, 1999. ACC139/1998

LEWIS, Andrew b. 1968
Ark Royale with Cheese, 2001 (1 of 8 works)
inkjet print on foam board; 8 works, each approx· 70·5 × 100·5; ed. 1/3;
purchased from Laurent Delaye Gallery, 2001. ACC7–14/2001

LEWIS, Dave b. 1962
Untitled (at Royal Anthropological Institute, London), 1995
c-type photograph; 101·6 × 76·2; ed. 2/5; purchased from the artist, 2001.
ACC1/2001

LEWIS, Tim b. 1961
Spin 1, 1989
wood, steel, electrical motor and plastic; 2 parts, each 129 × 54 × 56
(kinetic), base 72·5 × 54 × 54; purchased from Flowers East, 1989.
ACC30/1989

LEWIS, Tim b. 1961
Untitled Drawing, 1989
biro on paper; 25 × 16; purchased from Flowers East, 1989.
ACC31/1989

LEWITT, Sol
(see DIAMOND, Jessica)

LIJN, Liliane b. 1939
What is the sound of one hand clapping?, 1973 (still)
16mm film on Betacam sp video tape, running time: 14 minutes, ed. 6/200,
purchased from the artist, 2000. ACC50/1999

LINCOLN, Paul Etienne b. 1959
The World and Its Inhabitants, 1997
24 cards and small booklet in box; 13·5 × 8 × 2; ed. 1/24;
purchased from Book Works, 1999. ACC2/1999

LINCOLN, Paul Etienne b. 1959
The Globexpander – The Classification of Idle Courses, 1998
metal, nitrous oxide and mixed media; 30 × 10 × 10; ed. 9/24;
purchased from Book Works, 1999. ACC1/1999

LINCOLN, Paul Etienne b. 1959
The Violet Blooms of Ignisfatuus, 1998 (detail)
silkscreen in violet and ultra violet sensitive ink on vellum;
3 parts, each 41·3 × 33·7; ed. 3/29; purchased from the artist, 1999.
ACC3/1999

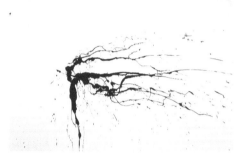

LINKE, Simon b. 1958
Untitled, 1993
oil on canvas; 94 × 107; purchased from Lisson Gallery, 1994.
ACC3/1994

I found the car keys on the marmalade lid in the fridge.

LINKE, Simon b. 1958
Lost, 1996
oil on canvas; 126·9 × 89·6;
purchased from Lisson Gallery, 1997. ACC50/1996

LIPSKI, Edward b. 1966
Tattoo, 1998
fibreglass, pig hide, ink, skin dye and steel; 65 × 107 × 35; ed. 3/3;
purchased from Entwistle Gallery, 1998. ACC72/1997

LIVINGSTONE, Richard b. 1951
Self Portrait, 1986
collograph and intaglio print; 80 × 60;
purchased from the artist, 1991. ACC21/1991

LIVINGSTONE, Richard b. 1951
Bisto the Consumer, 1989
collograph and intaglio print; 80 × 60;
purchased from the artist, 1991. ACC20/1991

LIVINGSTONE, Richard b. 1951
Unlikely Bedfellows, 1989
hessian, wood, metal, paint, wire, nylon and sisal; 112 × 123 × 12·2;
purchased from the artist, 1991. ACC19/1991

LOCHORE, Brad b. 1960
Shadow No.52, 1994
oil on canvas; 290 × 610; gift of Charles Saatchi, 1999.
ACC206/1998

LOCHORE, Brad
(see also BUGS portfolio)

LONDON PORTFOLIO   set of 11 prints; ed. 40/65; purchased from The Paragon Press, 1995

left to right, top to bottom

DENIS, Dominic b. 1963
Untitled, 1992
screenprint; 47 × 75 . ACC80/1995

FAIRHURST, Angus b. 1966
When I Woke up in the Morning the Feeling was Still There, 1992
screenprint; 86·5 × 65·8 . ACC81/1995

HIRST, Damien b. 1965
Untitled, 1992
screenprint; 86 × 62·4 . ACC82/1995

LANDY, Michael b. 1963
Cor! What a Bargain!, 1992
screenprint with marker-pen; 68·5 × 85·7 . ACC83/1995

LANGLANDS & BELL
(**LANGLANDS, Ben** b.1955 and **BELL, Nikki** b.1959)
Uno City, 1992
blind embossed screenprint; 71 × 74 . ACC84/1995

MAY, Nicholas b. 1962
Anabatic Print, 1992
screenprint; 75 × 47 . ACC85/1995

QUINN, Marc b. 1964
Template for My Future Plastic Surgery, 1992
screenprint; 86 × 68 . ACC86/1995

TAYLOR, Marcus b. 1964
Untitled, 1992
screenprint; 86 × 70·5 . ACC87/1995

TURK, Gavin b. 1967
Gavin Turk Right Hand and Forearm, 1992
screenprint; 86 × 68 . ACC88/1995

WHITEREAD, Rachel b. 1963
Mausoleum under Construction, 1992
screenprint; 66 × 86 . ACC89/1995

WOOD, Craig b. 1960
Safeway Gel-Air Freshener, Alpine Garden, 1992
screenprint with mould-cut sections; 66 × 86 . ACC90/1995

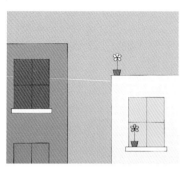

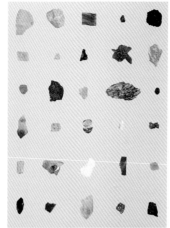

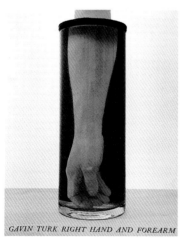

GAVIN TURK RIGHT HAND AND FOREARM

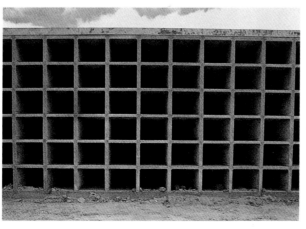

LOUDEN, Albert b. 1945
Untitled (single figure in a street), late 1990s
pastel on card; 54·5 × 80; purchased from England & Co, 1999.
ACC28/1998

LOWE, Rachel b. 1968
A Letter to an Unknown Person, No.5, 1998 (still)
Betacam sp video; running time: 1 minute, 30 seconds; ed. 3/3; purchased
from the artist, 2001. ACC19/2000

LUCAS, Sarah b. 1962
Self Portraits 1990–98
iris prints; 12 works; ed. 24/50; purchased from Sadie Coles HQ, 2000
© Sarah Lucus 2003. Courtesy Sadie Coles HQ London.

Eating a Banana 1990
78 × 82. ACC3/2000

Divine 1991
78·8 × 90·8. ACC4/2000

Self Portrait with Mug of Tea 1993
92·7 × 75. ACC6/2000

Self Portrait with Knickers 1994
98 × 73·1. ACC7/2000

Self Portrait with Fried Eggs 1996
98·2 × 73·7. ACC8/2000

Human Toilet II 1996
97·7 × 71·4. ACC9/2000

Fighting Fire with Fire 1996
97 × 73·3. ACC10/2000

Self Portrait with Skull 1997
97·3 × 70·8. ACC11/2000

Got a Salmon On #1 1997
98 × 72·5. ACC12/2000

Smoking 1998
97·3 × 71·6. ACC13/2000

Summer 1998
84·5 × 77·2. ACC14/2000

Human Toilet Revisited 1998
81·5 × 77·3. ACC15/2000

LUCAS, Sarah b. 1962
Willy, 2000 (installation shot)
plastic, tobacco, paper and glue; 86 × 42 × 34; purchased from Sadie Coles
HQ, 2002. ACC8/2002
© Sarah Lucus 2003. Courtesy Sadie Coles HQ London.

LUKE, Jeff 1962–95
Dowel and Wire, 1994
wood, wire, paper and grip-seal bag; 5 × 10·4 × 0·9, bag 13 × 11;
unlimited edition; purchased from Imprint, 1993. ACC29/1997
© Jeff Luke Estate 2003. Courtesy Jeff Luke Estate.

LUXEMBURG, Rut Blees b. 1967
Meet Me In Arcadia, 1996
c-print mounted on aluminium, printed 1998; 61 × 76; ed. 2/5; purchased
from Laurent Delaye Gallery, 1998. ACC37/1998

LYONS, John b. 1933
Victim of Papa Bois, 1990–92
oil on canvas; 146·6 × 127; purchased from the artist, 1996.
ACC46/1995

LYON, Marcus b. 1965
Chernobyl fallout still clouds future for UK sheep-farmers:
International Herald Tribune 4/6/88, 1992 (1 of 4 works)
selenium-toned print; 4 works, each 7 × 6; donated from the exhibition
Image '90s, 1992. ACC65–68/1993

McCANN, Pádraig b. 1963
Cryptbrick, 1991
oil on canvas; 4 parts, each 41·5 × 35·5; purchased from the artist, 1992.
ACC85/1991

McCONNELL, Richard b. 1959
Butcher Boy, 1992 (1 of 3 works)
black-and-white bromide print; 3 works, each 35·6 × 28; donated from
the exhibition *Image '90s*, 1992. ACC69–71/1993

MACDONALD, Ian b. 1946
South Gare Teesmouth, 1980
silver bromide print; 47·5 × 37·5; purchased from
Photographers' Gallery, 1994. ACC18/1994

McEWEN, Adam b. 1965
I Want to Live, 1993
suede and cotton; 23·9 × 10; unlimited edition; purchased from
Sarah Staton, 1994. ACC30/1997

MACH, David b. 1956
Battersea Chair 1, 1993
pencil on paper; 59.5 × 84; purchased from Jill George Gallery, 1995.
ACC28/1995

MACH, David b. 1956
Clad the Hayward, 1995
collage and pencil on paper; 80 × 111; purchased from Jill George Gallery,
1995. ACC29/1995

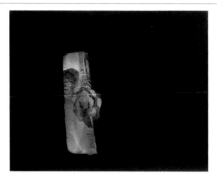

MacKAY, Calum Angus b. 1964
Frozen Heads I, 1992
silver gelatin print, printed 1995; 44 × 55.5; purchased from
Portfolio Gallery, 1995. ACC108/1995

MacKAY, Calum Angus b. 1964
Dog Chews, Roses, Half Dozen, 1993 (detail)
silver gelatin print, printed 1995; 3 parts, each 44 × 55.5; purchased
from Portfolio Gallery, 1995. ACC107/1995

MacKAY, Calum Angus b. 1964
Nailed Skate, 1993
silver gelatin print, printed 1995; 44 × 55.5; purchased from
Portfolio Gallery, 1995. ACC106/1995

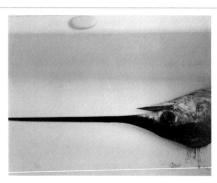

MacKAY, Calum Angus b. 1964
Swordfish/Soap, 1993
silver gelatin print, printed 1995; 44 × 55.5; purchased from
Portfolio Gallery, 1995. ACC109/1995

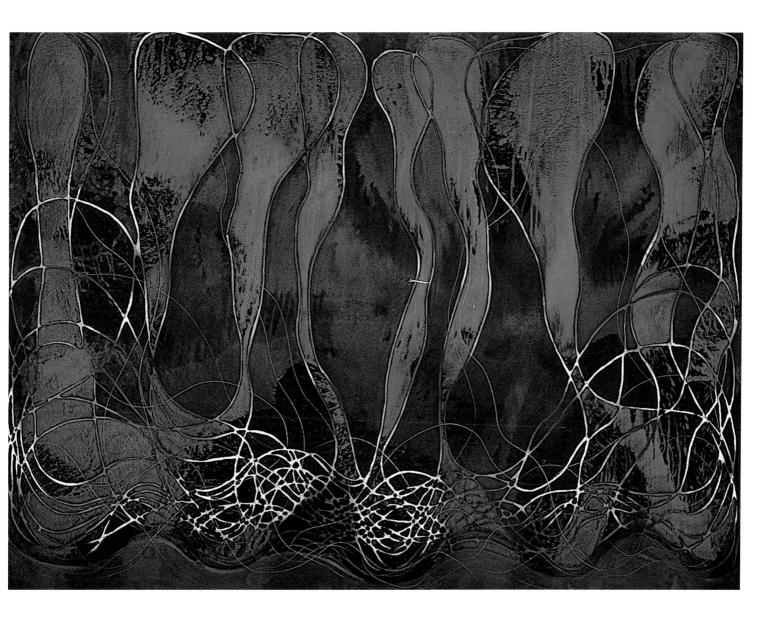

McKEEVER, Ian b. 1946
Assumptio (murmur), 1998—99
oil and acrylic on canvas; 245 × 330; purchased from Alan Cristea Gallery,
2000. ACC67/1999

MacKENNA, Tracey b. 1963
Havoc, 1996
wool; 250 × 143; purchased from Lotta Hammer, 1997. ACC18/1996

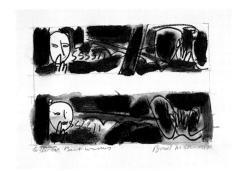

McLEAN, Bruce b. 1944
Drawing for Terrazzo Wall, Royal Festival Hall, 1988
watercolour and charcoal on paper; 56 × 75; gift of Joanna Drew, 1992.
ACC17/1992

McLEAN, Ian 1973–2000
Armour Jamais, 1996
oil on canvas; 218 × 218; gift of Charles Saatchi, 1999. ACC211/1998

McLEAN, Ian 1973–2000
Armour Rien, 1996
oil on canvas; 218 × 279; gift of Charles Saatchi, 1999. ACC210/1998

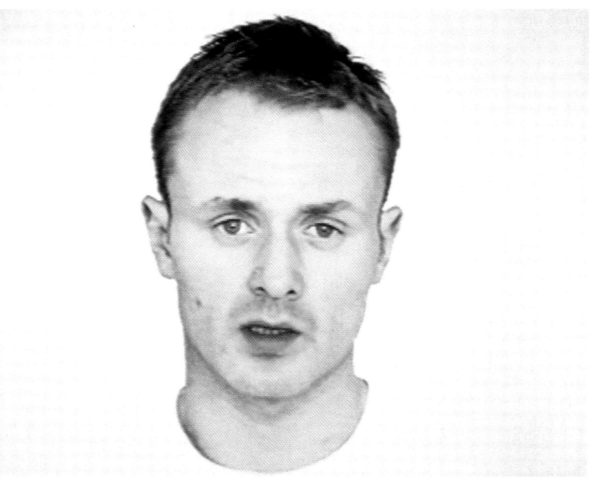

MacLEOD, Kenny b. 1967
Robbie Fraser, 1998 (still)
Betacam sp video tape; running time: 17 minutes; ed. 4/4;
purchased from the artist, 1999. ACC30/1999

MacLEOD, Kenny b. 1967
Twin Sisters, 1998 (still)
Betacam sp video tape; running time: 4 minutes; ed. 4/4;
purchased from the artist, 1999. ACC31/1999

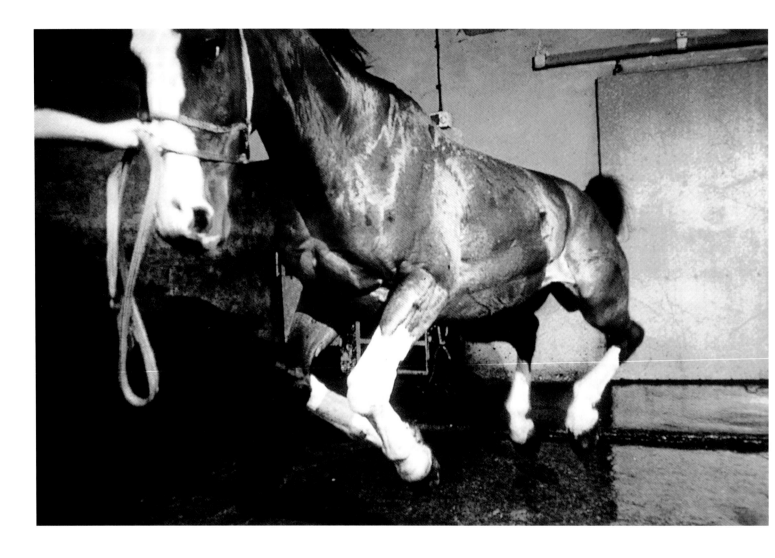

MacMILLAN, Tim b. 1959
Dead Horse, 1998 (still)
Betacam sp video tape looped projection; running time: 20 minutes; ed. 1/3;
purchased from Lux Centre, 1998. ACC20/1998

MAGILL, Elizabeth b. 1959
Without, 2002
oil on canvas; 91 × 122; purchased from Anthony Wilkinson Gallery, 2002.
ACC56/2002

McQUEEN, Steve b. 1969
Bear, 1993 (still)
16mm film/u-matic video transfer to Betacam sp video tape; running time:
10 minutes; purchased from Anthony Reynolds Gallery, 1995. ACC116/1995

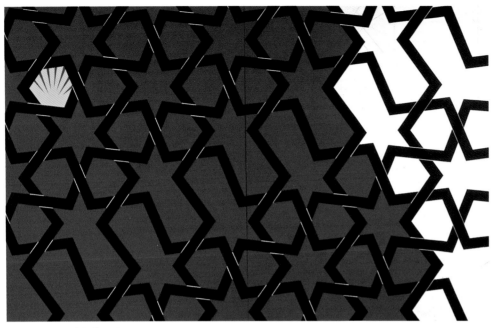

MAKHOUL, Bashir b. 1963
Zigzag, 1992
acrylic on canvas; 2 parts, total 230 × 350; purchased from
Huddersfield Art Gallery, 1994. ACC22/1994

MALINOWSKI, Antoni b. 1955
Not Titled, 1990
acrylic on canvas; 244 × 167.5; purchased from the artist, 1990.
ACC5/1990

MANCHOT, Melanie b. 1966
Mrs Manchot, Arms Overhead, 1996
silver gelatin print and mixed media on canvas; 193 × 140;
ed. 1/ 2; gift of Charles Saatchi, 1999.
ACC208/1998

MANCHOT, Melanie b. 1966
Mrs Manchot Stands Tall, 1996
silver gelatin print and mixed media on canvas;
2 parts, total 260 × 110; ed. 1/2; gift of Charles Saatchi, 1999.
ACC207/1998

MANSFIELD, Andrew b. 1953
Untitled No.130, 1995
oil on canvas; 152·9 × 137·7; purchased from
Anthony Reynolds Gallery, 1996. ACC45/1995

MARCHANT, Alison b. 1959
Charged Atmosphere, 1987
photograph on canvas, printed 1993; 212 × 302; purchased from Camden
Arts Centre, 1993. ACC18/1993

MARINKOV, Saša b. 1949
New Street Site, Bishopsgate, 1990
woodcut; 87·2 × 57·8; ed. 5/30; purchased from the artist, 1993.
ACC109/1997

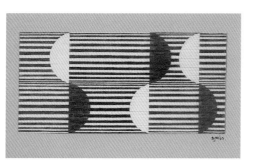

MARTIN, Barry b. 1943
Causal Rhythm, 1963
graphite on paper; 15·6 × 32·8; purchased from the artist, 2000.
ACC44/1999

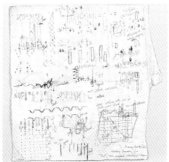

MARTIN, Barry b. 1943
Preparatory drawing for Series Revelation – 'Tret', 1965–66
pencil and pen on paper; 46 × 40; gift of the artist, 2000.
ACC45/1999

MASI, Denis b. 1942
Double Cross (study/red), 1990
mild steel, mirror, wire and etched cast glass; 54 × 70 × 25; purchased from
Anderson O'Day Gallery, 1991. ACC74/1991

MATISSE, Henri 1869–1954
Le Tobogan, from the Jazz *portfolio,* 1947 (1 of 20 works)
lithograph, facsimile of pochoir edition published by Tériade, Paris 1947
facsimile published by Georg Braziller; 20 pages, each 59·5 × 38·5;
ed. 57/250; purchased from Sotheby's, 1989. PR404
© Succession H Matisse / DACS 2003

MAUGHAN, Karl b. 1964
Aro Valley, 1999
oil on canvas; 228·5 × 259; purchased from The Approach, 1999.
ACC25/1999

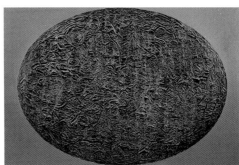

MAY, Nicholas b. 1962
Liminal Ellipse (orange), 1996
acrylic silicone and metallic powder on canvas; 213·5 × 320; gift of Charles
Saatchi, 1999. ACC209/1998

MAY, Nicholas
(see also LONDON portfolio)

MAY, Nicholas b. 1962
Guardians of Acheron, 1992
oil, resin and metallic powder on canvas; 274 × 244;
purchased from the artist, 1993. ACC13/1992

MEDALLA, David b. 1942
A Stitch in Time, 1968–72 (installation shot)
cotton, wood, steel and hemp installation; approx. 1,200 × 37; purchased
from the artist, 1991. ACC9/1990

MEDALLA, David b. 1942
A Prophecy, 1989
oil on canvas; 210 × 310; purchased from the artist, 1991. ACC10/1990

MEDALLA, David b. 1942
The Songs of Songs, 1999
c-type print and collage; 2 parts, each 122 × 173·8; purchased from the artist,
2000. ACC70/1999

MEDWAY, Jim b. 1974
Night Bus, 1999
ballpoint pen and indian ink on paper; 55 × 80; purchased from The Annual
Programme, 1999. ACC42/1998

MEDWAY, Jim b. 1974
Shoe Shop, 1999
ballpoint pen and indian ink on paper; 55 × 80; purchased from The Annual
Programme, 1999. ACC41/1998

MELLIS, Margaret b. 1914
Wild Poppies: Blue Shadow, 1987
oil pastel on paper; 26 × 24·4; purchased from
Austin/Desmond Fine Art, 2001. ACC37/2000

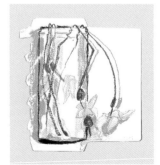

MELLIS, Margaret b. 1914
Dying Daffodils, 1989
oil pastel on paper; 25 × 23·4; purchased from
Austin/Desmond Fine Art, 2001. ACC36/2000

MINNIS, Michael b. 1964
Irish Liberation in Shades of Red, 1989
oil on canvas; 266·7 × 233·5; purchased from the artist, 1991.
ACC3/1991

MINNIS, Michael b. 1964
Untitled, 1989
oil on canvas; 274·3 × 228·6; purchased from the artist, 1991.
ACC21/1990

MITHA, Alnoor b. 1961
Ascension, 1983
oil on canvas; 121·5 × 121·5; purchased from the artist, 1996.
ACC51/1995

MONK, Jonathan b. 1969
My Glasses, 1994
plastic, metal and glass; 4·4 × 14·2 × 14·8; unlimited edition; purchased
from the artist, 1994. ACC45/1997

MONKS, John b. 1954
Car Door in a Landscape, 1989–90
oil on canvas; 228·6 × 152·4; anonymous gift, 1990.
ACC1/1990

MONTAG, Daro b. 1959
Reform, 1992 (1 of 2 works)
silver gelatin print; 2 works, each 45·5 × 34·5; donated from
the exhibition *Image '90s*, 1992. ACC73–74/1993

MOORE, Joan 1909–97
Pelican, 1993
enamelled steel; 22 × 19 × 12; gift of Kenneth Armitage, 1998.
ACC78/1997

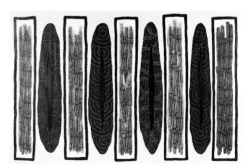

MORETON, Vic b. 1951
Archive, 1989
wax and acrylic on canvas; 193 × 303; purchased from the artist, 1992.
ACC81/1991

MORGAN, Tony b. 1938
Vulnerability, 1996
oil and acrylic on canvas; 220 × 61;
purchased from the artist, 1999. ACC28/1999

MORGAN, Tony b. 1938
Le Mot, 1997
oil and acrylic on canvas; 24·5 × 75; purchased from the artist, 2000.
ACC46/1999

MORGAN, Tony b. 1938
Non docteur, je ne suis pas un beefsteak, 1999 * (1 of 9 works)
woodcut with aquatint; 9 works, each 35 × 25; ed. 3/3; purchased from the
artist, 2000. ACC2/2000

MUNDY, Henry b. 1919
Untitled, 1990
acrylic on canvas; 180 × 76·5; purchased from
Nigel Greenwood Gallery, 1991. ACC39/1991

MURPHY, Stephen b. 1962
Untitled, 1994 (installation shot)
dye sublimination photographic print; 15 parts,
from 8·9 × 8·5 to 14·1 × 8·9; ed. 1/3; gift of Charles Saatchi, 1999.
ACC212/1998

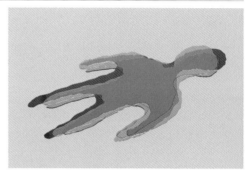

MUSGRAVE, David b. 1973
Overlapping Figures, 2001
acrylic; 0·3 × 96 × 57; ed. 2/3; purchased from greengrassi, 2001.
ACC41/2001

NAPIER, Philip b. 1965
Sawing Away at the Fiddle, 1989
steel, rubber and wood (kinetic); 70 × 50 × 50;
purchased from the artist, 1991. ACC22/1990

NEAGU, Paul b. 1938
HH: Human Hand Impulses and Vectors, 1972
ink and pencil on canvas; 20·3 × 20·3; purchased from the artist, 1989.
ACC33/1989

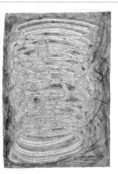

NEAGU, Paul b. 1938
Human Condition, 1977
watercolour on gesso-coated canvas; 43·3 × 31·3; purchased from the artist,
1989. ACC34/1989

NELSON, Mike b. 1967
Taylor, 1994 (installation shot)
metal, canvas, wood and mixed media; 250 × 336 × 456; purchased from
Matt's Gallery, 1997. ACC58/1997

NEUDECKER, Mariele b. 1965
Eclipse, 1994
card with photographs, glass, Tippex, wood and light fittings; 100 × 22·5 × 22·5; purchased from Whitechapel Art Gallery, 1996. ACC3/1996

NEUDECKER, Mariele b. 1965
Stolen Sunsets, 1996
steel, glass, fibreglass, dye, acrylic, enamel, water, salt and varnish; 180 × 65 × 45; gift of Charles Saatchi, 1999. ACC227/1998

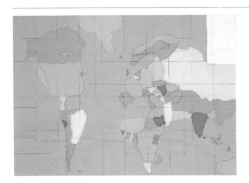

NEUDECKER, Mariele b. 1965
Never Eat Shredded Wheat (Memory Maps), 1996 *
(1 of 9 works)
acrylic and felt-tip pen on paper, aluminium map pins; 9 works, each 82 × 112; purchased from Whitechapel Art Gallery, 1996. ACC64–72/1996

NEWMAN, Avis b. 1946
Bird Box – "La Scatola dell'Uccello", 1992
wood, glass and steel; 98 × 73 × 13·5; purchased from Lisson Gallery, 1992. ACC3/1993

NICHOLSON, Seamus b. 1971
Leisure Lounge, 1996
c-type print on aluminium; 152 × 102; ed. 4/10; purchased from The Agency, 2000. ACC47/1999

NICHOLSON, Seamus b. 1971
Megatripolis, 1996
c-type print on aluminium; 102 × 152; ed. 5/10; purchased from The Agency,
2001. ACC38/2001

NIEMIS, Renato b. 1958
Blind Faith, 1992 (installation shot)
mixed media; 244 × 244 × 366; gift of Charles Saatchi, 1999.
ACC228/1998

NIMKI, Jacques b. 1959
Florilegium, 1999
graphite on paper; 193 × 150·5; purchased from
The Approach, 1999. ACC26/1999

NOGUEIRA, Lucia 1950–98
Two into One Won't Go, 1993
MDF, watercolour on paper and felt; 86·4 × 218·4 × 53·3; purchased from
Anthony Reynolds Gallery, 1993. ACC8/1993

NOGUEIRA, Lucia 1950–98
One and Three, 1994 (detail)
glass, mercury, phosphorus, paint, platinum, velvet and cardboard;
2 earrings, each 5·2 × 1 × 1·8, box: 3·1 × 8·1 × 8·1; ed. 1/13;
purchased from the artist, 1994. ACC46/1997

NOGUEIRA, Lucia 1950–98
Binocular, 1996 (installation shot)
plywood, blackboard paint, 21 umbrellas, 7 kites, r-type photograph and
video; 2 kiosks, each 247 × 116 × 124, photograph 100 × 70; running time:
5 minutes; purchased from Anthony Reynolds Gallery, 1996. ACC13/1996

O'CONNELL, Deirdre b. 1956
No Fire in the Hearth, No Sun in the South I, 1985
charcoal and pastel on paper; 137·1 × 101·6; purchased from the artist, 1991.
ACC31/1991

O'CONNELL, Deirdre b. 1956
No Fire in the Hearth, No Sun in the South II, 1985
charcoal and pastel on paper; 137·1 × 101·6; purchased from the artist, 1991.
ACC32/1991

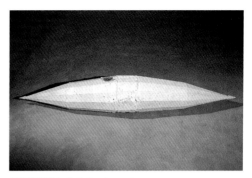

O'CONNELL, Deirdre b. 1956
Big Dark Boat, 1989
plaster, linen, pigment and beeswax; 40 × 233 × 37; purchased from the artist, 1991. ACC30/1991

OBUABANG, Henry b. 1969
Obuabang SRS: B Painting No.8 (Art from the Heart), 1991
acrylic on canvas; 110 × 110; purchased from the artist, 1992. ACC89/1991

OFILI, Chris b. 1968
The Visit, 1993 * (1 of 10 works)
etching; 10 works, each 38 × 29; purchased from the artist, 1994.
ACC8–17/1994

OFILI, Chris b. 1968
Popcorn Shells, 1995
paper collage, oil, polyester resin, map-pins and elephant dung on linen and
2 elephant dung props; 182·9 × 121·9 × 15·8; purchased from Victoria Miro
Gallery, 1996. ACC58/1995

OPIE, Julian b. 1958
Indirect Lighting, 1989
rubber, aluminium, glass, plastic, wood, stainless steel and fluorescent light;
187 × 125 × 40; purchased from Lisson Gallery, 1989. ACC24/1989

OPIE, Julian b. 1958
Do you ever think of me?, 1996 * (1 of 3 works)
colour print, glass and aluminium; 3 works, each 48 x 83·4; ed. 1/3;
purchased from Lisson Gallery, 1997. ACC38–40 /1996

OPIE, Julian b. 1958
This is Fiona, 2000 (still)
computer film on CD-ROM, computer and wall-mounted screen; ed. 1/3;
purchased from Lisson Gallery, 2001. ACC45/2000

OTA, Tsugumi b. 1951
The Death of Hyacinthus, 1990
woodcut; 91·5 × 61; ed. 1/30; purchased from
Jill George Gallery, 1993. ACC108/1997

OTHER MEN'S FLOWERS PORTFOLIO set of 15 prints and title pages; ed. 47/50; purchased from Factual Nonsense, 1995

left to right, top to bottom

page 160

COMPSTON, Joshua 1970–96
Title page, 1994
woodblock; 61 x 47 . ACC61/1995

COMPSTON, Joshua 1970–96
First Introductory Page, 1994
woodblock; 61 x 47. ACC62/1995

COMPSTON, Joshua 1970–96
Second Introductory Page, 1994
woodblock; 61 x 47. ACC63/1995

COMPSTON, Joshua 1970–96
Colophon Page, 1994
woodblock; 61 x 47. ACC64/1995

BOND, Henry b. 1966
Untitled, 1994
letterpress; 61 x 47. ACC65/1995

BRISLEY, Stuart b. 1933
Untitled, 1994
letterpress; 47 x 61. ACC66/1995

BROWN, Don b. 1962
Untitled, 1994
monotype; 47 x 61. ACC67/1995

CHADWICK, Helen 1953–96
Untitled, 1994
letterpress; 47 x 61. ACC68/1995

COLLISHAW, Mat b. 1966
Untitled, 1994
letterpress; 61 x 47. ACC69/1995

DORON, Itai b. 1967
Untitled, 1994
letterpress; 61 x 47. ACC70/1995

page 161

EMIN, Tracey b. 1963
Untitled, 1994
letterpress; 47 x 61. ACC71/1995

FAIRHURST, Angus b. 1966
Untitled, 1994
letterpress; 47 x 61. ACC72/1995

GILLICK, Liam b. 1964
Untitled, 1994
letterpress; 47 x 61. ACC73/1995

HERMAN, Andrew b. 1961
Untitled, 1994
screenprint; 61 x 47. ACC74/1995

HUME, Gary b. 1962
Untitled, 1994
screenprint; 47 x 61. ACC75/1995

STATON, Sarah b. 1961
Untitled, 1994
letterpress; 61 x 47. ACC76/1995

TAYLOR-WOOD, Sam b. 1967
Untitled, 1994
letterpress; 47 x 61. ACC77/1995

TURK, Gavin b. 1967
Untitled, 1994
screenprint; 47 x 61. ACC78/1995

WIGRAM, Max b. 1966
Untitled, 1994
screenprint; 47 x 61. ACC79/1995

OTHER MEN'S FLOWERS

OTHER MEN'S FLOWERS
A TEXT PUBLICATION BY FIFTEEN LONDON BASED ARTISTS

CURATED BY
JOSHUA COMPSTON

Henry Bond
Stuart Brisley
Don Brown
Helen Chadwick
Mat Collishaw
Itai Doron
Tracey Emin
Angus Fairhurst
Liam Gillick
Andrew Herman
Gary Hume
Sarah Staton
Sam Taylor-Wood
Gavin Turk
Max Wigram

PUBLISHED BY
THE PARAGON PRESS

adore abhor

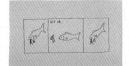

Herman Kahn is director of the RAND Institute
JK Galbraith is Ambassador to India
Fiddle and Faddle have something to hide
Robert McNamara has the place to hide it

McNamara

A Picasso Pictures and Plus de Lumiere! production
Produced by Daniele Buttinmore and Jane Bolton
Director of animation Michael Salkeld
Associate Producer (France) Charles de Meaux
Written and directed by Liam Gillick

AAAAAARR
RRRRRRGG
GGGGGGHH
HHHHHHH
HHHHH!!!

Evening Standard

I Walked The world of
CAPITALIST REALITY HANG
Up YOUR tireD SomBRErO

TakinG LUcKY
& making it
plain
or The
CenSOR's
ERROR

cloSed
SyStem

VOID speak

Cunt.

CHARNEL

PACKARD, Simon b. 1960
Birmingham, 1993
woodcut; 117× 91; ed. 2/20; purchased from the artist, 1993.
ACC107/1997

PALMER, Eugene b. 1955
The Laughing Christ, 1991
oil on canvas; 2 parts, total 137·1 × 221·3; purchased from the artist, 1993.
ACC4/1993

PANCHAL, Shanti b. 1951
Mannequin, 1990
watercolour on paper; 79 × 98; purchased from the artist, 1998.
ACC13/1998

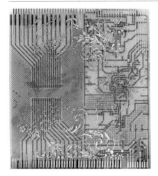

PARKER, Cornelia b. 1956
Small Thought, 1994
printed circuit board, silver components; 36 × 30 × 12; ed. of 50; purchased
from the artist, 1994. ACC47/1997

PARKER, Cornelia
(see also BUGS portfolio)

PARKER, Cornelia b. 1956
Meteorite Lands on..., 1998 *
printed and burned paper; 5 works, each 54 × 69; edition of 20; purchased
from the Multiple Store, 1999; A Multiple Store Commission.
ACC29–33/1998

Meteorite Lands on Buckingham Palace, 1998 * (illustrated)
ed. 5/20. ACC30/1998

PARKER, Jayne b. 1957
Crystal Aquarium, 1995 (still)
Betacam sp from 16mm black-and-white film; running time: 33 minutes;
purchased from the artist, 1997. ACC4/1997

PARSONS, Jonathan b. 1970
Achrome, 1994
polyester, cotton, wood and rope; 457 × 228;
gift of Charles Saatchi, 1999. ACC229/1998

PARSONS, Vicken b. 1957
Untitled, 2000
oil on birch plywood panel; 15 × 20; purchased from the artist, 2002.
ACC5/2002

PARSONS, Vicken b. 1957
Untitled, 2001
oil and charcoal on birch plywood panel; 15 × 20; purchased from the artist,
2002. ACC6/2002

PATTERSON, Richard b. 1963
Motocrosser, 1995
oil and acrylic spray paint on canvas; 3 parts, total 208.3 × 315; purchased
from Anthony d'Offay Gallery, 1995. ACC6/1995

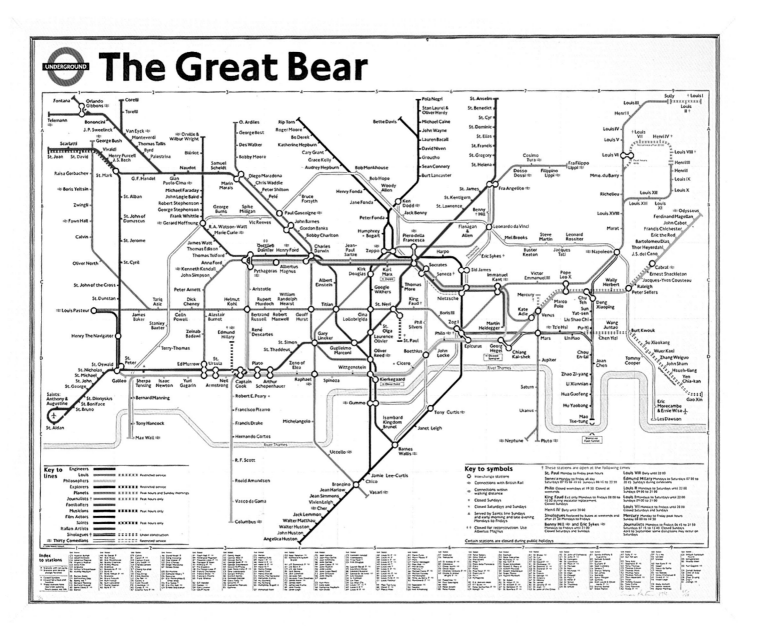

PATTERSON, Simon b. 1967
The Great Bear, 1992
lithograph on paper in anodized aluminium frame; 109·2 × 134·5; ed. 25/50;
purchased from the artist, 1993. ACC10/1993
© Simon Patterson and Transport for London 2003

PAYNE, Oliver b. 1977 and **RELPH, Nick** b. 1979
Mixtape, 2002 (still)
DVD; running time: 23 min; ed. 11/20; purchased from
Gavin Brown's Enterprise, 2002. ACC57/2002

PEERS, Angela b. 1953
The Audience, 1991
glass, steel, plastic and leather; 120 × 250 × 5; purchased from
Laure Genillard Gallery, 1992. ACC92/1991

PENALVA, João b. 1949
Huckleberry, 1992
2 parts, part 1: tempera, oil and encaustic wax on canvas, part 2: oil and
encaustic wax on photocopies on paper, velvet collage, glass and wood;
part 1: 161 × 66·3 × 3·5, part 2: 135·7 × 107·7; purchased from the artist,
1993. ACC7/1992

PERITON, Simon b. 1964
SP, 1995
foil paper; 55·9 × 53·3; purchased from ICA, 1998. ACC21/1998

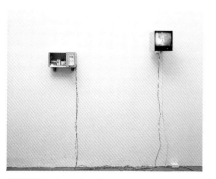

PERKINS, Gary b. 1967
Meanwhile, at the Marie Curie School of Organic Chemistry...,
1995
monitor, CLD camera and mixed media; 17·4 × 32·5 × 24; gift of
Charles Saatchi, 1999. ACC230/1998

Meanwhile, at the Marie Curie School of Organic Chemistry...,
1995 (detail)

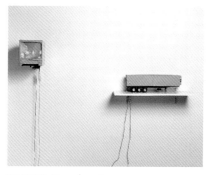

PERKINS, Gary b. 1967
-15° C at 60 mph, 1996
monitor, CLD camera and mixed media; 16 × 10 × 55; purchased from
Victoria Miro Gallery, 1997. ACC14/1996

PERRY, Grayson b. 1960
Spirit Jar, 1994
earthenware; 45·7 × 20·3 × 20·3; purchased from Laurent Delaye Gallery,
2002. ACC11/2002

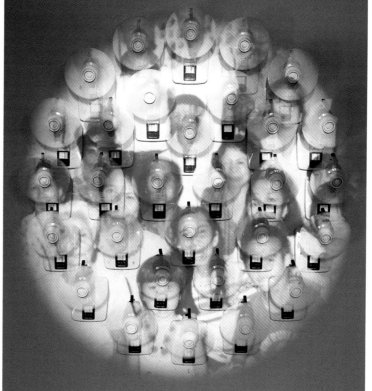

PHAOPHANIT, Vong b. 1961
Fragments, 1990 (installation shot)
mixed media, 30 electric ventilator fans and 160 slides;
projected image: 200 diameter; purchased from the artist, 1990.
ACC3/1990

PHILLIPS, Tony b. 1952
The History of the Benin Bronzes, 1984 * (1 of 10 works)
etching; 10 works, each 21·3 × 26·5; purchased from the artist, 1989.
ACC1–10/1989

PHOKELA, Johannes b. 1966
Candle Bathing, 1997
oil on board; 121·7 × 102; purchased from Rack Gallery, 1998.
ACC2/1998

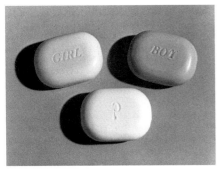

PIGOTT, Hadrian b. 1961
Boy, ?, Girl, 1994
soap; 3 parts, each 3 × 8·3 × 5·9; unlimited edition; purchased from Sarah
Staton, 1994. ACC31/1997

PIGOTT, Hadrian b. 1961
Dysfunction, 1994
soap, plumbing components and plastic; 3 parts, each, 41 × 63·5 × 43;
gift of Charles Saatchi, 2002. ACC39/2002

top
PIGOTT, Hadrian b. 1961
Submersive I, 1994
soap, steel and polystyrene; 30·5 × 178 × 61; gift of Charles Saatchi, 2002.
ACC40/2002

bottom
PIGOTT, Hadrian b. 1961
Submersive II, 1994
soap, steel, polystyrene and plastic; 28 × 170 × 67; gift of Charles Saatchi,
2002. ACC41/2002

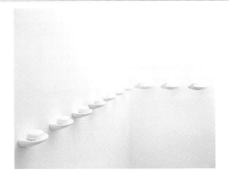

PIGOTT, Hadrian b. 1961
Wash I (Self – Position 1 – London 23rd March 1994), 1994
(installation shot)
soap and painted plaster; 18 parts, each 8 × 13 × 8·5; gift of Charles Saatchi,
1999. ACC233/1998

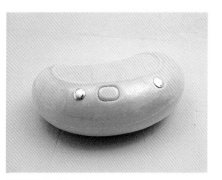

PIGOTT, Hadrian b. 1961
Blank III, 1995
soap, plastic shrink-wrap and chromed plastic; 30 × 85 × 45;
gift of Charles Saatchi, 1999. ACC231/1998

PIGOTT, Hadrian b. 1961
Fleeting, 1995
fibreglass, relief panel with flocked surface; 225 × 300 × 12;
gift of Charles Saatchi, 1999. ACC232/1998

PIGOTT, Hadrian b. 1961
Instrument of Hygiene (case 2), 1995
velvet, fibreglass, leatherette, ceramic, brass and chrome; 50 × 70 × 40;
purchased from the artist, 1995. ACC16/1995

PIPER, Keith b. 1960
Four Corners, a Contest of Opposites, 1995
computer montage prints on transparency film in lightboxes; 4 parts, each
182·9 × 50·8 × 53·3, installation dimensions variable; purchased from the
artist, 2000. ACC78/1999

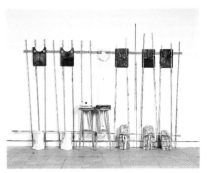

PLACKMAN, Carl b. 1943
Any Place to Hang your Hat: Wedlock, 1978
mixed media with wood, plaster, slate, cloth, glass and strip light; 340 × 350 × 35; gift of the Arnolfini Collection Trust, 2001. ACC65/2000

POLLARD, Ingrid b. 1953
Pastoral Interlude, No.4, 1988 (detail)
hand-tinted silver print and text; 51 × 51; purchased from the artist, 2000. ACC56/1999

POLLARD, Ingrid b. 1953
Pastoral Interlude, No.5, 1988 (detail)
hand-tinted silver print and text; 51 × 51; purchased from the artist, 2000. ACC57/1999

PONCELET, Jacqui b. 1947
Carpet, 1992
wool; 1 × 512·5 × 280; purchased from the artist, 1993. ACC6/1992

POPE, Nicholas b. 1949
Judas Font, 1995
glazed terracotta, concrete and steel; 75 × 150 × 80, base (not illustrated) 155 high; purchased from the artist, 1998. ACC11/1998

PORTER, Michael b. 1948
Fungus and Silver Birch, 1989–90
mixed media on canvas; 2 parts, total 200 × 343; purchased from Pomeroy Purdy Gallery, 1991. ACC13/1990

POWER, Mark b. 1959
The Fluffers, 1992 (1 of 2 works)
silver gelatin print; 2 works, each 40 × 50; donated from the exhibition *Image '90s*, 1992. ACC75–76/1993

PRADA, Ana b. 1965
Striped Composition no.2, 1995–98
wax, silicone and MDF; 192 × 39 × 1; purchased from the artist, 1998. ACC67/1997

PRENDERGAST, Kathy b. 1958
Land, 1990
canvas, fabric, paint, pencil, wood and metal; 234 × 620 × 358;
purchased from the artist, 1991. ACC35/1991

PRENDERGAST, Kathy b. 1958
The End and the Beginning, 1996
human hair and wood; 5.5 × 4 × 4; ed. 2/3; purchased from
Kerlin Gallery, 1997. ACC21/1996

PRENDERGAST, Kathy b. 1958
Hair Bonnet, 1997
human hair; 13 × 20 × 20; ed. 2/3; purchased from
Kerlin Gallery, 1997. ACC22/1996

PRENDERGAST, Kathy
(see also BUGS portfolio)

PRICE, Joanna b. 1956
Blue Pietà, 1992
oil on canvas; 183 × 183; gift of Charles Saatchi, 1999.
ACC234/1998

PYKE, Steve b. 1957
Philosophers, 2000
multi-toned silver gelatin print; 61 × 51; purchased from Light Industry,
2002. ACC10/2002

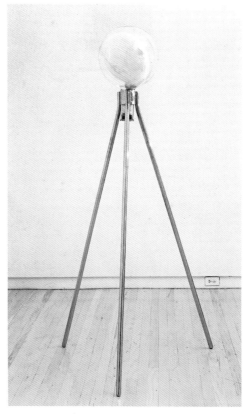

QUINN, Marc b. 1964
I Need an Axe to Break the Ice, 1992
latex rubber, glass and stainless steel; 187 × 94 × 76; gift of Charles Saatchi,
2002. ACC42/2002

QUINN, Marc
(see also LONDON portfolio)

QUINN, Marc b. 1964
Garden² (no.1) – (no.8), 2000 *
pigment ink-jet print with varnish; 8 works, each 80·6 × 124·5; ed. 40/45;
purchased from The Paragon Press, 1995

Garden²(no.1), 2000 *
ACC20/2000

Garden² (no.2), 2000 *
ACC21/2000

Garden² (no.3), 2000 *
ACC22/2000

Garden² (no.4), 2000 *
ACC23/2000

Garden² (no.5), 2000 *
ACC24/2000

Garden² (no.6), 2000 *
ACC25/2000

Garden² (no.7), 2000 *
ACC26/2000

Garden² (no.8), 2000 *
ACC27/2000

RAE, Fiona b. 1963
Untitled (pale green I), 1990
oil on canvas; 213·5 × 198·2; purchased from Waddington Galleries, 1991.
ACC40/1991

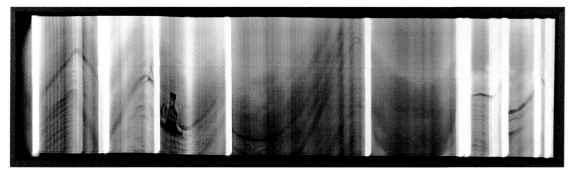

READ, Simon b. 1949
Woodbridge Haven Buoy No.2, 1988
c-type photograph; 69 × 274; ed. 1/5; purchased from James Hockey Gallery, 1991. ACC1/1991

REDDICK, Peter b. 1924
Pan and Luna, 1969
wood engraving; 7 3 × 6; ed. 13/24; purchased from the artist, 1993. ACC105/1997

REEDY, Carlyle b. 1938
A Very Early, 1968
torn card and card collage with newsprint; 24 × 30; purchased from the artist, 1999. ACC129/1998

REEDY, Carlyle b. 1938
Word, c.1974
collage, manuscript, paint and tissue paper; 28 × 21; purchased from the artist, 1999. ACC130/1998

REEDY, Carlyle b. 1938
No Title, c.1977
collage, paper and fabric; 22 × 28; purchased from the artist, 1999. ACC126/1998

REEDY, Carlyle b. 1938
Precession of the Equinoxes, c.1982
collage and crayon; 20·5 × 26·5; purchased from the artist, 1999. ACC127/1998

REEDY, Carlyle b. 1938
Line-Tie, 1984–85
collage; 14·5 × 21·5; purchased from the artist, 1999. ACC128/1998

REGO, Paula b. 1935
Old King Cole (from *The Nursery Rhymes* series, 1989)
(1 of 5 works)
etching with aquatint; 5 works, each 21·5 × 22·5; ed. 21/50; purchased from
Marlborough Graphics, 1990.
ACC53/1990 from series ACC53–54/1990 and ACC57–59/1990

RELPH, Nick
(see PAYNE, Oliver)

RENSHAW, Tim b. 1964
Returning, 1994
oil on canvas; 244 × 183; purchased from the artist, 1998. ACC62/1997

RHODES, Carol b. 1959
Industrial Landscape, 1997
oil on board; 42·5 × 47·5; purchased from Andrew Mummery Gallery, 1997.
ACC56/1997

RHYS JAMES, Shani b. 1953
Stare, 1997
oil on gesso on board; 30 × 27·6; purchased from the artist, 1997.
ACC50/1997

RICE, Bernard 1900-98
Six Slav Heads, 1925 (1 of 6 works)
woodcut; 6 works, each approx· 13·8 × 11·5, paper approx· 20 × 17·8;
ed. 12/50; purchased from the artist, 1993. ACC115–120/1997

RIDDY, John b. 1959
Barcelona, 1991
gelatin silver print; 34 × 27; ed. 1/8; purchased from
Frith Street Gallery, 1995. ACC112/1995

RIDDY, John b. 1959
Milan, 1993
gelatin silver print; 34 × 27; ed. 1/8; purchased from
Frith Street Gallery, 1995. ACC113/1995

RIDDY, John b. 1959
Milan, 1993
gelatin silver print; 34 × 27; ed. 1/8; purchased from
Frith Street Gallery, 1995. ACC114/1995

RIDDY, John b. 1959
Perugia, 1993
gelatin silver print; 34 × 27; ed. 2/8; purchased from
Frith Street Gallery, 1995. ACC5/1995

RIDDY, John b. 1959
New York, 1994
gelatin silver print; 34 × 27; ed. 1/8; purchased from
Frith Street Gallery, 1995. ACC115/1995

RIELLY, James b. 1956
Object of Fun, 1995
oil on canvas; 213·1 × 183; gift of Charles Saatchi, 1999.
ACC235/1998

RIELLY, James b. 1956
Daddy, I Love You, 1996
oil on canvas; 81·2 × 71·1; purchased from Laurent Delaye Gallery, 1996.
ACC6/1996

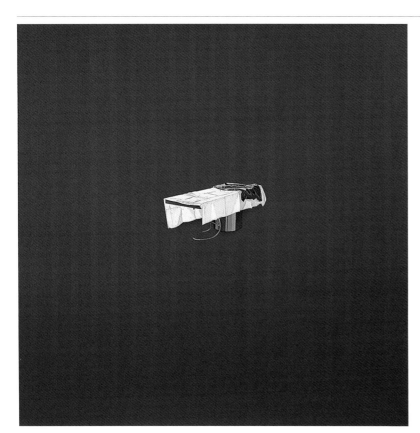

ROBERTS, Julie b. 1963
Mortuary Table (green), 1994
oil and acrylic on canvas; 150 × 150; purchased from Interim Art, 1995.
ACC110/1995

ROBERTS, Perry b. 1954
Untitled, 1988
cotton duck, linen and cotton; 89·5 × 89·5 × 21; purchased from David Thorp, 1992. ACC96/1991

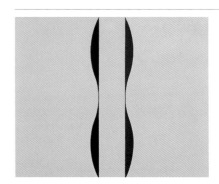

ROBERTSON, Carol b. 1955
Over and Under, 1990
oil and wax on canvas; 122 × 153; purchased from the artist, 1991.
ACC34/1991

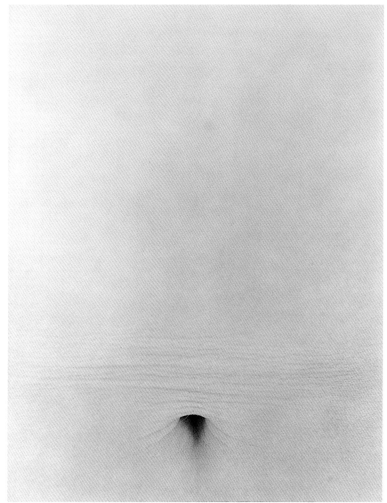

ROBERTSON, Helen b. 1959
Navel, 1994
black-and-white photograph mounted on aluminium, printed 1995;
177 × 138; ed. 1/3; purchased from the artist, 1996. ACC48/1995

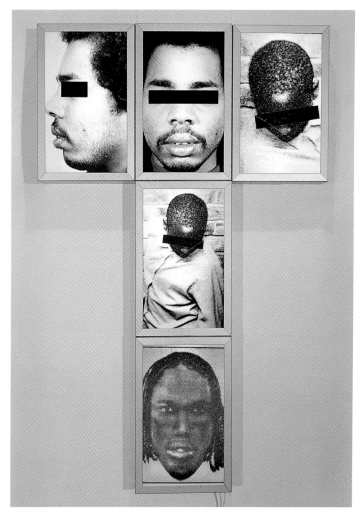

RODNEY, Donald 1961–98
Self-Portrait "Black Men Public Enemy", 1990
lightboxes with Dyratran prints; 5 parts, total 190·5 × 121·9; purchased from
the artist, 1990. ACC7/1990
© Estate of Donald Rodney 2003

RODNEY, Donald 1961–98
In the House of My Father, 1997
photographic print on aluminium; 153 × 122; ed. 1/3; purchased from
the Trustees of the Estate of Donald Rodney, 1999. ACC59/1997
© Estate of Donald Rodney 2003

ROME, Richard b. 1943
Nubian 1, 1980
bronze; 33·2 × 24·5 × 18·5; ed. 1/4
purchased from the artist, 1998. ACC26/1998

ROSSI, Mario b. 1958
The End/Untitled, series 1996–2000
acrylic on canvas; 61 × 86·5; purchased from the artist, 2001.
ACC24/2001

ROSSI, Mario b. 1958
The End/Untitled, series 1996–2000
acrylic on canvas; 61 × 86·5; purchased from the artist, 2001.
ACC25/2001

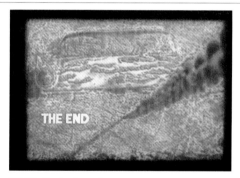

ROSSI, Mario b. 1958
The End/Untitled, series 1996–2000
acrylic on canvas; 61 × 86·5; purchased from the artist, 2001.
ACC26/2001

ROSSI, Mario b. 1958
The End/Untitled, series 1996–2000
acrylic on canvas; 61 × 86·5; purchased from the artist, 2001.
ACC27/2001

ROSSI, Mario b. 1958
The End/Untitled, series 1996–2000
acrylic on canvas; 61 × 86·5; purchased from the artist, 2001.
ACC28/2001

ROUGH, Gary b. 1972
Space, 1995
paint, photographs, paper, wood, glass, metal and plastic; dimensions variable; gift of Charles Saatchi, 1999. ACC236/1998

RUSHTON, Emma b. 1965
Chris (Businessmen), 1992
Plasticard, printed paper, perspex, paint and MDF; 158·8 × 24·3 × 24·3; gift of Charles Saatchi, 1999. ACC238/1998

RUSHTON, Emma b. 1965
Raphe (Businessmen), 1992
Plasticard, printed paper, perspex, gravel, paint and MDF; 114 × 30 × 20; gift of Charles Saatchi, 1999. ACC237/1998

RÜTHI, Andreas b. 1956
Goya (toy), 1997
oil on MDF; 30 × 40; purchased from the artist, 1998. ACC63/1997

RYAN, Veronica b. 1956
Lamentations in the Garden, 2000 (detail)
acrylic on silver bromide print; 5 parts, each approx. 43 × 27·9; purchased from the artist, 2001. ACC37/2001

SADOTTI, Giorgio b. 1955
Giorgio's Balls (1–9), 1994 * (1 of 9 works)
watercolour on paper; 9 works, each 25·4 × 35·5; purchased from Interim Art, 1995. ACC97–105/1995

SAUNDERS, Nina b. 1958
Hidden Agenda, 1994
upholstery materials, dustpan and brush, fabric, cotton, metal, wood and plastic; 68·5 × 68·5 × 79; gift of Charles Saatchi, 2002. ACC43/2002

SAUNDERS, Nina b. 1958
Ladies Waiting Room, 1995
plastic, foam and wood; 78 × 117 × 60; gift of Charles Saatchi, 2002. ACC44/2002

SAUNDERS, Nina b. 1958
Unfinished Opera, 1996
plastic, fabric, cotton and wood; 69 × 57 × 108; gift of Charles Saatchi, 1999. ACC239/1998

SAVALIEV, Boris b. 1948
Woman Worker in Painted Cab of Machine, n.d.
c-type print; 30·7 × 30·6; purchased from the artist, 1990. ACC56/1990

THE SCOTTISH BESTIARY PORTFOLIO

set of 20 prints with text by George Mackay Brown
all sheets 76 × 56; ed. 15/60; purchased from The Paragon Press, 1987

BELLANY, John b. 1942
Eagle, 1986
etching; 45 × 29.9. ACC7/1987

BELLANY, John b. 1942
Grouse, 1986
etching; 45.1 × 29.8.
ACC10/1987

BELLANY, John b. 1942
Wildcat, 1986
etching; 45.4 × 30.1.
ACC23/1987

CAMPBELL, Steven b. 1953
Frontispiece, 1986
woodcut; 56.5 × 38.5 . ACC9/1987

CAMPBELL, Steven b. 1953
Lobster, 1986
woodcut; 56.2 × 38.8. ACC12/1987

HOWSON, Peter b. 1958
Fieldmouse, 1986
lithograph; 54.7 × 36.9. ACC8/1987

HOWSON, Peter b. 1958
Moth, 1986
lithograph; 54.3 × 36.5. ACC13/19

HOWSON, Peter b. 1958
Stag, 1986
lithograph; 55 × 37 . ACC19/1987

KNOX, John b. 1936
Dove, 1986
lithograph; 53.3 × 35.5. ACC5/1987

KNOX, John b. 1936
The Nuckelavee, 1986
lithograph; 53.6 × 35.6. ACC14/1987

KNOX, John b. 1936
Whale, 1986
lithograph; 53.5 × 35.6. ACC22/19

McLEAN, Bruce b. 1944
Salmon, 1986
screenprint; 32·8 × 32·3. ACC16/1987

McLEAN, Bruce b. 1944
Spider, 1986
screenprint; 37 × 35. ACC18/1987

McLEAN, Bruce b. 1944
Stoor-worm, 1986
screenprint; 36·1 × 37·4. ACC20/1987

REDFERN, June b. 1951
Lion, 1986
lithograph; 59·5 × 44·2. ACC11/1987

REDFERN, June b. 1951
Seal, 1986
lithograph; 59·7 × 38·2. ACC17/1987

REDFERN, June b. 1951
Wolf, 1986
lithograph; 61·5 × 37·5. ACC24/1987

WISZNIEWSKI, Adrian b. 1958
Dragon, 1986
lithograph; 53·3 × 34·6. ACC6/1987

WISZNIEWSKI, Adrian b. 1958
Raven, 1986
screenprint; 53·2 × 35·7. ACC15/1987

WISZNIEWSKI, Adrian b. 1958
Unicorn, 1986
etching; 51·5 × 33·8. ACC21/1987

SCREEN PORTFOLIO   set of 11 prints; ed. 14/45 purchased from The Paragon Press, 1998

© the artists and The Paragon Press 2003

left to right, top to bottom

ALMOND, Darren b. 1977
Multiple Working, 1997
embossed screenprint; 73 × 89. ACC121/1997

CHAPMAN, Jake b.1966 and **CHAPMAN, Dinos** b. 1962
Double Deathshead, 1997
screenprint; 71 × 86.5. ACC122/1997

COLLISHAW, Mat b. 1966
Untitled, 1997
screenprint; 86 × 57. ACC123/1997

GALLACCIO, Anya b. 1963
Broken English August '91, 1997
screenprint; 68 × 88.5. ACC124/1997

HAPASKA, Siobhán b. 1963
Untitled, 1997
screenprint; 58 × 89. ACC125/1997

LANE, Abigail b. 1967
Dinomouse Sequel Mutant X, 1997
screenprint; 57 × 88.5. ACC126/1997

STARR, Georgina b. 1968
You Stole My Look, 1997
screenprint; 89 × 72. ACC127/1997

TAYLOR-WOOD, Sam b. 1967
Red Snow, 1997
screenprint; 75 × 89. ACC128/1997

WEARING, Gillian b. 1963
The Garden, 1997
screenprint; 61 × 89. ACC129/1997

WYN EVANS, Cerith b. 1958
The Return of the Return of the Durutti Column, 1997
screenprint; 74 × 88. ACC130/1997

YASS, Catherine b. 1963
Stage, 1997
screenprint; 89 × 74. ACC131/1997

Darren James Almond

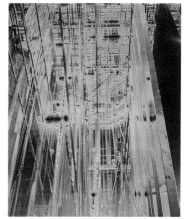

SCULLION, Louise
(see DALZIEL, Matthew)

SEAR, Helen b. 1955
The Surface Beneath, 1991
r-type hand print, black-and-white print and LEDs; 3 parts, total 92 × 336;
ed. 1/2; purchased from The Showroom, 1992. ACC94/1991

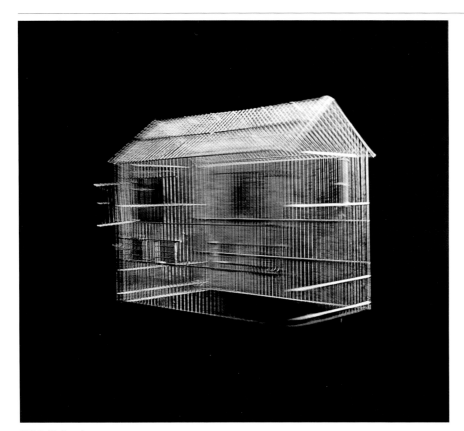

SEAR, Helen b. 1955
Flown No.1, 1997
c-type print on MDF; 127·9 × 91·4; ed. 1/3; purchased from Zelda Cheatle
Gallery, 1997. ACC49/1997

SEAWRIGHT, Paul b. 1965
(Tuesday 3rd April 1973) from the *Sectarian Murder* series,
1988–91 * (1 of 15 works)
c-type print with text, printed 1991; 15 works, each 101·6 × 76·2; purchased
from the artist, 1991. ACC4–17/1991

SEDGLEY, Peter b. 1930
Corona, 1970 (installation shot)
PVA and pigment on canvas, optional lights (kinetic); 200 × 200; gift of the
Arnolfini Collection Trust, 2001. ACC69/2000

SEDIRA, Zineb b. 1963
Self Portraits or the Virgin Mary (from the *Self Portrait* series),
2000
c-type photograph; 3 parts, each 182·9 × 101·6; ed. 3/5; purchased from the
artist, 2002. ACC3/2002

SHIRAISHI, Yuko b. 1956
Dewfall, 1990
oil on canvas; 244 × 183; purchased from Edward Totah Gallery, 1991.
ACC23/1990

SHONIBARE, Yinka
(see BUGS portfolio)

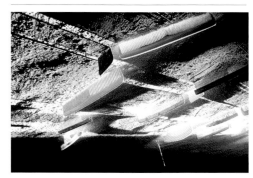

SHORT, Louise b. 1964
Teething Room, 1999 (installation shot)
plastic, 16mm projector; dimensions variable; purchased from the
artist, 2000. ACC48/1999

SHRIGLEY, David b. 1968
Take off…, 1997
marker on paper; 15 × 10; purchased from
Galleri Nicolai Wallner, 1999. ACC36/1999

SHRIGLEY, David b. 1968
*These and others will be there to greet you
at the airport…, 1997*
marker on paper; 15 × 10; purchased from
Galleri Nicolai Wallner, 1999. ACC37/1999

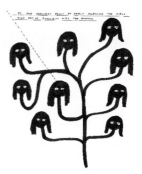

SHRIGLEY, David b. 1968
At the earliest point of early morning…, 1998
marker on paper; 24 × 21; purchased from
Galleri Nicolai Wallner, 1999. ACC34/1999

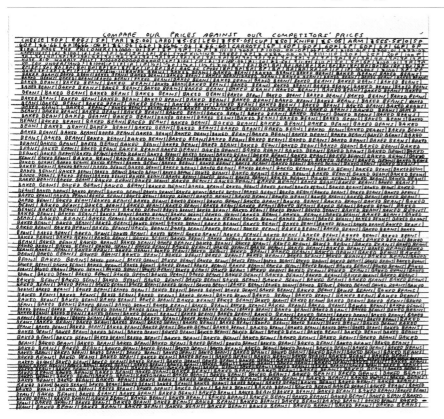

SHRIGLEY, David b. 1968
Compare our prices against our competitors…, 1998
marker on paper; 24·5 × 26; purchased from Galleri Nicolai Wallner, 1999.
ACC32/1999

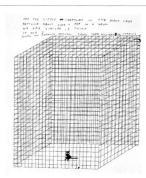

SHRIGLEY, David b. 1968
See the little creature in the giant cage…, 1998
marker on paper; 24 × 21; purchased from
Galleri Nicolai Wallner, 1999. ACC33/1999

SHRIGLEY, David b. 1968
The road to beasthood…, 1998
marker on paper; 24 × 20·5; purchased from
Galleri Nicolai Wallner, 1999. ACC35/1999

SIKAND, Gurminder b. 1960
Figure and Head, 1994
gouache on paper; 28·5 × 40·5; purchased from Kapil Jariwala Gallery, 1996.
ACC52/1995

SIKAND, Gurminder b. 1960
Untitled II, 1994
gouache on paper; 34 × 41·7; purchased from Kapil Jariwala Gallery, 1996.
ACC53/1995

SILVERMAN, Lynn b. 1952
ICI Works, 1996 (no. 8 from the *Corporation House* series,
1995–99) (1 of 6 works)
black-and-white photograph; 6 works, each 61·5 × 79; purchased from the
artist, 1999. ACC131–136/1998

SIMPSON, Jane b. 1965
Between, 1992
wood, brass, plastic, ice, refrigeration units, castors and steel;
127 × 115·5 × 62; gift of Charles Saatchi, 1999. ACC240/1998

SIMPSON, Jane b. 1965
Baby Bath (lip slightly melted), 1996
silicone rubber, formica and plinth; 15 × 52 × 39·5; ed. 1/3;
purchased from Laurent Delaye Gallery, 1996. ACC8/1996

SINCLAIR, Ross b. 1966
T-Shirt Paintings 1–80, 1993–98 (installation shot)
gesso and acrylic on cotton; 80 parts, each approx 61 × 61; purchased from
the artist, 1999. ACC43–122/1998

ALTHOUGH JANIS JOPLIN WAS C
OMPLEETLY DEAF AND REALLY O
LD SHE WAS STILL ABLE TOWRITE
TWO OFHER BEST SONG STRAWB
ERRY FIELDS FOREVER(I CANT GET
NO)SATISFACTION AND MY WAY

SMITH, Bob and Roberta b. 1962
Although Janis Joplin...(Idiot Board), 1997
signwriters' paint on board; 4 parts, total 243·8 × 487·7; purchased from the
artist, 1998. ACC69/1997

SMITH, Bob and Roberta b. 1962
Make Art Not War, 1997 (still)
VHS video; running time: 11 minutes; ed. 1/5; purchased from the artist,
1998. ACC66/1997

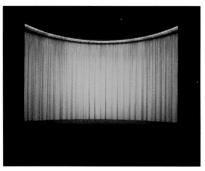

SMITH, Bridget b. 1966
Odeon (Green), 1995
c-type print on MDF; 183 × 183; ed. 2/3; purchased from Frith Street Gallery,
1995. ACC49/1995

SMITH, Bridget b. 1966
Premier, 1995
c-type print on MDF; 183 × 183; ed. 2/3; purchased from Frith Street Gallery,
1995. ACC50/1995

SMITH, Emma b. 1968
Scum, 1996 (detail)
bromide print; 5 parts, total 29 × 492; ed. 1/3; purchased from Laure
Genillard Gallery, 1997. ACC36/1996

SMITH, Kate b. 1955
Who could have guessed there'd be so much diversity?, 1991
glass, tafetta, nylon, thread and metal; 30.5 × 30.5 × 32.5;
purchased from Matt's Gallery, 1998. ACC22/1998

SMITH, Stephanie
(see STEWART, Eddie)

SOUTHAM, Jem b. 1950
The Raft of Carrots, 1990 (1 of 4 works)
c-type photograph, printed 2001; 4 works, each 50·8 × 61;
unnumbered ed. of 10; purchased from the artist, 2001.
ACC48/2000 from series ACC48-51/2000

SOUTHAM, Jem b. 1950
Birling Gap, 2000
c-type photograph, printed 2001; 2 parts, each 100 × 150; ed. 2/6;
purchased from the artist, 2001. ACC32/2000

STAHL, Andrew b. 1954
Close, 1998
oil on canvas; 198 × 229; purchased from
Angela Flowers Gallery, 1998. ACC9/1998

STARLING, Simon b. 1967
Kabinett für Zeichnung, 1995
charcoal, paper and tape; purchased from the artist, 1997. ACC54/1997

STARR, Georgina b. 1968
Mentioning, 1992
script, score and tape; 20·5 × 14·7, tape 10·8 × 6·9 × 1·7;
unnumbered ed. of 100; purchased from Anthony Reynolds Gallery, 1994.
ACC32/1997

STARR, Georgina b. 1968
The Nine Collections of the Seventh Museum, 1994
(installation shot)
SFA3 colour photographs, silkscreen, paint on paper and printed paper; 13
parts; photographs 40 × 50, posters 175 × 118 and catalogue; purchased
from Anthony Reynolds Gallery, 1995. ACC34/1995

STARR, Georgina
(see also SCREEN portfolio)

STATON, Sarah b. 1961
How the West has Won and Lost, 1999
bleach on denim; 180 × 140; purchased from the artist, 2001.
ACC36/2001

STATON, Sarah
(see also OTHER MEN'S FLOWERS portfolio)

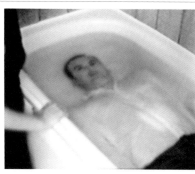

STEWART, Eddie b. 1961 and **SMITH, Stephanie**
b. 1968
Mouth to Mouth, 1995 (still)
black-and-white monitor, u-matic video tape; running time: 60 minutes;
ed. 2/3; purchased from the artists, 1999. ACC12/1999

STEWART, Kerry b. 1965
This Girl Bends, 1996
fibreglass and enamel paint; 147 × 63 × 55; ed. 3/3; purchased from Stephen
Friedman Gallery, 1996. ACC11/1996

STEWART, Kerry b. 1965
Untitled (Lucy), 1996
fibreglass and enamel paint; 152 × 50 × 35;
gift of Charles Saatchi, 1999. ACC241/1998

STOCKHAM, Jo b. 1961
An Early Start, 1989–90
plywood, wallpaper, steel and lead; 2 parts, each 86 × 122·5 × 122·5;
purchased from the artist, 1991. ACC46/1991

STUBBING, N.H. (Tony) 1921–83
Untitled, 1958
oil on canvas; 60 × 72·5; purchased from England & Co, 1992.
ACC88/1991

STUTTGEN, Johannes
(see DAHN, Walter)

SULTER, Maud b. 1960
Calliope (from the *ZABAT* series), 1989
cibachrome print; 152·4 × 121·9; purchased from the artist, 1991.
ACC11/1990

SULTER, Maud b. 1960
Terpsichore (from the *ZABAT* series), 1989
cibachrome print; 152·4 × 121·9; purchased from the artist, 1991.
ACC100/1991

SUTTON, Trevor b. 1948
Friendship, 1990
oil on board; 61·8 × 61·8; purchased from the artist, 1991.
ACC47/1991

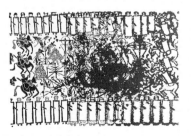

SYKES, Sandy b. 1944
Stain, 1987
woodcut; 50·1 × 75·8; ed. 9/50; purchased from the artist, 1993.
ACC106/1997

TAYLOR, Marcus
(see also LONDON portfolio)

TAYLOR-WOOD, Sam
(see OTHER MEN'S FLOWERS portfolio and SCREEN portfolio)

TAYLOR, Marcus b. 1964
Untitled (Upright Fridge), 1991
acrylic sheet; 124 × 66 × 61; gift of Charles Saatchi, 1999.
ACC242/1998

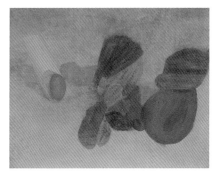

THESIGER, Amanda b. 1964
Arrangement, 1994
oil on canvas; 84 × 107; purchased from Francis Graham-Dixon Gallery, 1995.
ACC37/1995

TILLYER, William b. 1938
Waterfall 6, 1976
watercolour on paper; 104 × 38;
gift of Arnolfini Collection Trust, 2001.
ACC63/2000

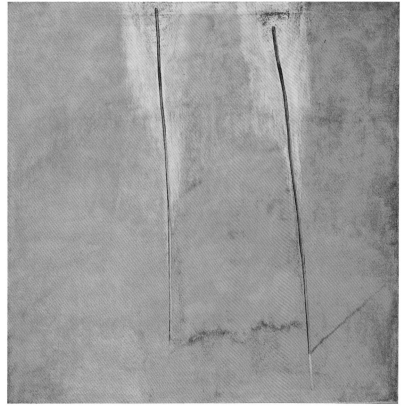

THOMPSON, Estelle b. 1960
Virgin Ground, 1988
oil on canvas; 152 × 152·5; purchased from Pomeroy Purdy Gallery, 1991.
ACC14/1990

TILLYER, William b. 1938
Waterfall 17, 1976
watercolour on paper; 104 × 38;
gift of Arnolfini Collection Trust, 2001.
ACC64/2000

TILLYER, William b. 1938
Waterfall 24, 1976
watercolour on paper; 104 × 38;
gift of Arnolfini Collection Trust, 2001.
ACC62/2000

TIMONEY, Pádraig b. 1968
Untitled, 1991
MDF, paint, collage, filter and turf; 2 parts, total 42 × 9·5 × 9;
purchased from Laure Genillard Gallery, 1992. ACC93/1991

TITCHNER, Mark b. 1973
*Something Plastic to Fight the Invisible (English Language Golem
Perimeter)*, 2001 (installation shot)
wool, nails, wood, light fittings and bulbs; 4 parts, each 125 × 30 × 30,
fifth part, 125 × 30 × 100; purchased from Vilma Gold, 2001. ACC5/2001

TOREN, Amikam b. 1945
Of the Times – 28 January 1993, 1993
pulped paper and PVA on canvas; 234 × 220; purchased from Anthony
Reynolds Gallery, 1993. ACC2/1993

TRANGMAR, Susan b. 1953
Untitled Landscape, 1985–86
(from the *Untitled Landscapes* series)
cibachrome print; 76·2 × 101·6; purchased from the artist, 1999.
ACC76/1999

TRANGMAR, Susan b. 1953
Untitled Landscape, 1986
(from the *Untitled Landscapes* series)
cibachrome print; 76·2 × 101·6; purchased from the artist, 1999.
ACC75/1999

TURK, Gavin b. 1967
Oi!, 1998
r-type photograph; 3 parts, each 244 × 197; ed. 3/3; purchased from White
Cube, 1999. ACC25/1998

TURK, Gavin
(see also BUGS portfolio, LONDON portfolio and
OTHER MEN'S FLOWERS portfolio)

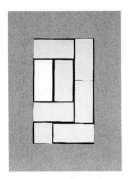

TURNBULL, Alison b. 1956
Hagi (from the *Little Japanese Paintings* series), 2000
oil and acrylic on canvas; 58·4 × 43·2; purchased from
Mobile Home, 2000. ACC17/2000

TYSON, Ian b. 1933
Ming, 1988 (1 of 8 works)
screenprint; 8 works, each 31·5 × 24 + cover sheet; ed. 2/15;
purchased from the artist, 1992. ACC83/1991

TYSON, Ian b. 1933
Three Vertical Prints, 1989/90 (1 of 3 works)
screenprint; 3 works, each 104 × 34; purchased from the artist, 1992.
ACC82/1991

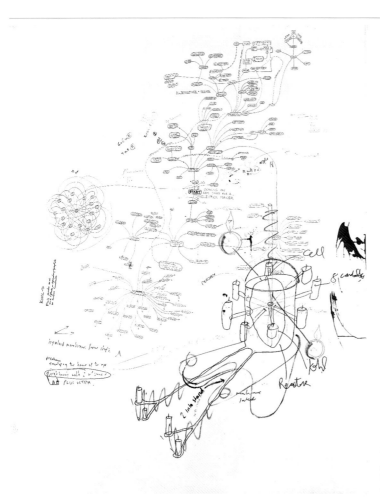

TYSON, Keith b. 1969
Applied Artmachine Chart: Candlestick Maker, 1999
ballpoint pen, felt-tip pen, ink and pencil on paper; 157 × 126; purchased
from Anthony Reynolds Gallery, 2000. ACC16/2000

URKOM, Gera b. 1940
Apple painting with hyacinth blue brush stroke, 1986
acrylic on canvas; 164 × 165·2; purchased from the artist, 1991.
ACC76/1991

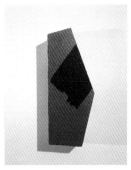

URKOM, Gera b. 1940
Small segment – red with black brush stroke
(from the *Defamiliarisation of the Apple* series), 1988
acrylic on canvas, wood and plaster; 40·1 × 15·8 × 8·7; purchased from the
artist, 1991. ACC79/1991

URKOM, Gera b. 1940
Medium segment – red with black brush stroke
(from the *Defamiliarisation of the Apple* series), 1990
acrylic on canvas, wood and plaster; 105 × 59·3 × 16·5; purchased from the
artist, 1991. ACC78/1991

URKOM, Gera b. 1940
Red segment with in-the-centre brush stroke
(from the *Defamiliarisation of the Apple* series), 1991
acrylic on canvas, wood and plaster; 121·9 × 121·9 × 20·3; purchased from
the artist, 1991. ACC77/1991

VALDIVIA, Marco b. 1947
Untitled, 1989–92
acrylic on wood and canvas; 21·2 × 28·5; gift of the artist, 1998.
ACC253/1998

VALDIVIA, Marco b. 1947
Oda a Los Mapuches, 1994
acrylic on wood and canvas; 21·2 × 28·5; purchased from the artist, 1999.
ACC35/1998

VALDIVIA, Marco b. 1947
Oda a Tehuiriche, 1994
acrylic on wood and canvas; 21·2 × 28·5; purchased from the artist, 1999.
ACC36/1998

VERRAN, Virginia b. 1961
Pink Painting No.1, 1995
oil on canvas; 228 × 198; purchased from
Francis Graham-Dixon Gallery, 1996. ACC60/1995

VILAINCOUR, Leon b. 1923
Jean Pierre Latz / Jeanne Lanvin, 1993–94
oil on canvas; 121·9 × 111·8; purchased from the artist, 1997.
ACC59/1996

VINER, Darrell 1946–2001
The Grind, 1984
stone, metal, electronic motor and electronics; 35·5 × 23 × 30·5 (kinetic);
purchased from the artist, 1992.
ACC97/1991

VIRTUE, John b. 1947
Landscape 301, 1966
acrylic, black ink, shellac emulsion and earth on canvas; 275 × 330;
gift of the Arnolfini Collection Trust, 2001. ACC67/2000

VOORSANGER, Jessica b. 1965
David Cassidy's Diet, 1994
rice, rubber, tetracycline and polythene; 3.2 × 19.4 × 20.9; ed. 50;
purchased from *Sarah Staton's Superstore*, Laure Genillard Gallery, 1994.
ACC33/1997

VOORSANGER, Jessica b. 1965
Susan Dey's Beauty Tips, 1994
biscuits, toothpaste, pills and polythene; 3.2 × 20.9 × 17.5; ed. 50;
purchased from *Sarah Staton's Superstore*, Laure Genillard Gallery, 1994.
ACC34/1997

WAKELY, Shelagh b. 1932
Angel, 1984
ink on paper; 153 × 122; purchased from the artist, 1999. ACC38/1998

WALKER, Ian b. 1952
Little Chef, Astley, East Lancs Road, Nr. Manchester, 1984
c-type photograph, printed 1999; 21 × 29.5; purchased from the artist,
2000. ACC53/1999

WALKER, Ian b. 1952
Little Chef, Redbrook, Wye Valley, 1984
c-type photograph, printed 1999; 21 × 29.5; purchased from the artist,
2000. ACC52/1999

WALLINGER, Mark b. 1959
Heaven, 1988
brass, painted metal, gravel and aluminium; 175.5 × 68 × 37;
purchased from Anthony Reynolds Gallery, 1993. ACC9/1993

WALLINGER, Mark b. 1959
A Real Work of Art, 1994
wood, brass, polyurethane, plastic and paint; 12 × 12.8 × 7.3; unnumbered
ed. of 50; purchased from Anthony Reynolds Gallery, 1994. ACC35/1997

WALLINGER, Mark b. 1959
Angel, 1997 (still)
projected Betacam sp video/film; running time: 7 minutes, 30 seconds;
ed. 5/10; purchased from Anthony Reynolds Gallery, 1997. ACC1/1997

WALLINGER, Mark
(see also BUGS portfolio)

WALLINGER, Mark b. 1959
The Four Corners of the Earth, 1998 (installation shot)
slide projections on canvas; 4 parts, each 218 diameter, installation
dimensions variable; ed. 1/4; purchased from Anthony Reynolds Gallery,
1999. ACC24/1998

WARD, David b. 1951
Imagination Dead Imagine, 1991 (detail)
one way surveillance mirror and silkscreen; 8 parts, each 33 × 25;
purchased from the artist, 1994. ACC2/1994

WARREN, Rebecca b. 1965
Journey into the Heart of the Night, 2000
unfired clay, neon and mixed media; 44 × 140 × 39;
purchased from Interim Art, 2002. ACC7/2002

WEARING, Gillian b. 1963
Confess all on video. Don't worry you will be in disguise.
Intrigued? Call Gillian..., 1994 (still)
Betacam sp video tape; running time: 30 minutes; ed. 5/10;
purchased from Interim Art, 1997. ACC42/1996

WEARING, Gillian b. 1963
60 Minutes Silence, 1996 (still)
laser disc back-projection video; running time: 60 minutes; projection size:
365·8 × 548·6; purchased from Interim Art, 1997. ACC41/1996

WEARING, Gillian
(see also SCREEN portfolio)

WEBB, Gary b. 1973
Clap, 1997
plastic, aluminium, microphone and electrical components;
25 × 36 × 10; gift of Charles Saatchi, 2002. ACC45/2002

WEBB, Gary b. 1973
Island, 1997
glass, carpet and wood; approx. 44 × 20 × 20 and plinth;
gift of Charles Saatchi, 2002. ACC46/2002

WEBB, Gary b. 1973
Mr Little Tree, 1997
plastic, wood, chrome, personal stereo and cassette (sound);
137 × 120 × 84; gift of Charles Saatchi, 2002. ACC47/2002

WEBB, Gary b. 1973
Lovers, 1998
aluminium and plastic; 76 × 36 × 26;
gift of Charles Saatchi, 2002. ACC48/2002

WEBB, Gary b. 1973
DON'T KNOW WHY BUT STOP LOOKING AT, 1998
plastic and brass; 170 × 260 × 2; gift of Charles Saatchi, 2002.
ACC49/2002

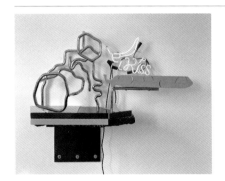

WEBB, Gary b. 1973
Mirage of Loose Change, 2001
chrome, steel, plastic, granite, wood and neon light; 108 × 132 × 47;
purchased from The Approach, 2001. ACC2/2002

WEBB, Mary b. 1939
Spring Colour Study No.19, 1995
oil on canvas; 112 × 112; purchased from the artist, 1997.
ACC7/1997

WEBBER, Denise b. 1958
Clay, 1998 (still)
Betacam sp film; running time: 4 minutes, 30 seconds; ed. 1/3;
purchased from the artist, 2001. ACC29/2001

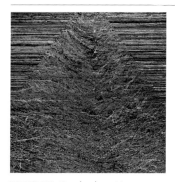

WEBSTER, Catrin b. 1966
Level Playing Fields, 1995–96
oil on canvas; 259.1 × 259.1; purchased from the artist, 1997.
ACC51/1997

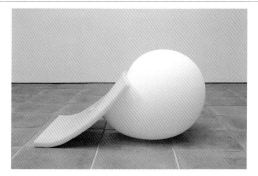

WEIDLE, Carina b. 1966
Blank and Flat, 1992
rubber and wax; 46 × 100 × 70; gift of Charles Saatchi, 1999. ACC243/1998

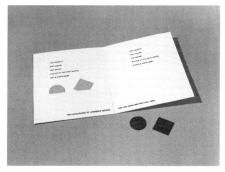

WEINER, Lawrence b. 1941
Twixt One (&) the Other, 1992
printed card and metal; 15.5 × 13; unlimited edition; purchased from
G-W Press, 1994. ACC36/1997

WEINER, Lawrence
(see also DIAMOND, Jessica)

WENTWORTH, Richard b. 1947
Guide, 1984
rubber and concrete; 42 × 33 × 12; purchased from Lisson Gallery, 1989.
ACC25/1989

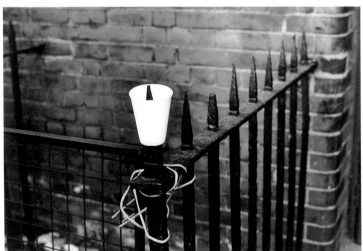

WENTWORTH, Richard b. 1947
London, 1999. Making do and getting by., 2000
unique photograph; 74 × 92 × 6.5; purchased from Lisson Gallery, 2001.
ACC60/2000

WENTWORTH, Richard b. 1947
Tirana, 1999. Occasional Geometries., 2000
unique photograph; 74 × 92 × 6.5; purchased from Lisson Gallery, 2001.
ACC61/2000

WHITEREAD, Rachel b. 1963
Untitled, 1993
bronze; 6·3 × 6·3 × 20·3; ed. 1/14; purchased from Karsten Schubert Gallery,
1994. ACC37/1997

WHITEREAD, Rachel
(see also LONDON portfolio)

WHITEREAD, Rachel b. 1963
Untitled Six Spaces, 1994 (installation shot)
resin; 6 parts, from 42 × 29 × 28·2 to 40 × 48·5 × 41·5; purchased from
Karsten Schubert Gallery, 1995. ACC96/1995

WIGRAM, Max
(see OTHER MEN'S FLOWERS portfolio)

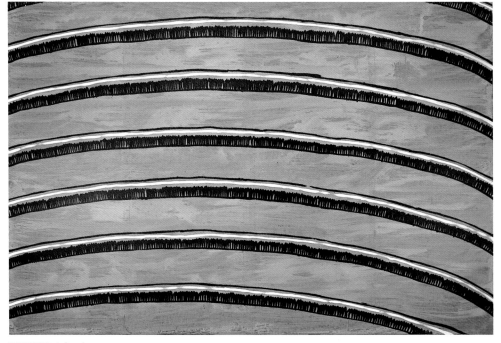

WILKINS, John b. 1951
Dancing in the Dark, 1993
acrylic on canvas; 244 × 366; gift of Charles Saatchi, 1999. ACC245/1998

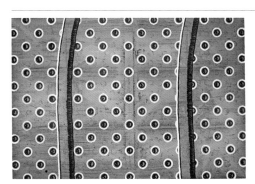

WILKINS, John b. 1951
Winterwonderland, 1993
acrylic on canvas; 244 × 366; gift of Charles Saatchi, 1999. ACC244/1998

WILKINS, John b. 1951
Was Wondering, 1995
acrylic on canvas; 244 × 183; purchased from
Anthony Reynolds Gallery, 1996. ACC47/1995

WILLIAMS, Emrys b. 1958
To the Lighthouse No.13, December/January, 1994–95
acrylic on paper; 127 × 109; purchased from the artist, 1997. ACC46/1996

WILLIAMS, Lois b. 1953
One Room Living, 1985 (installation shot)
sacking, felt, wadding and mixed media; box 34·3 × 26·7 × 26·5,
work 34·3 × 134·6 × 129·5; purchased from the artist, 1997. ACC53/1997

WILLIAMSON, Erlend 1965–96
Escape Stories (Mont Blanc Massive), 1995–96
c-type print; 30 × 20; ed. 1/10; purchased from Mrs Barbara Williamson,
1997. ACC5/1997
© Estate of Erlend Williamson 2003

WILSON, Chris b. 1959
All Will Be Forgotten, 1987
mixed media on board; 101·5 × 68·6;
purchased from the artist, 1991. ACC17/1990

WILSON, Chris b. 1959
In October Light, 1987
mixed media on board; 101·8 × 76·2;
purchased from the artist, 1991. ACC16/1990

WILSON, Chris b. 1959
Interior World, 1987
mixed media on board; 101·7 × 68·6;
purchased from the artist, 1991. ACC18/1990

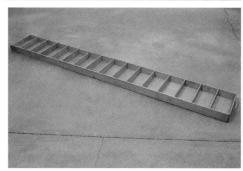

WILSON, Chris b. 1959
Some Day You Will Be One Of Those Who Lived Long Ago, 1987
mixed media on board; 101·8 × 68·7;
purchased from the artist, 1991. ACC15/1990

WILSON, Chris b. 1959
North, 1989–90
mixed media on board; 71 × 71; purchased from the artist, 1991.
ACC19/1990

WILSON, Hilary b. 1963
Drawer III, 1990
wood; 9·5 × 310 × 38·5; purchased from *New Contemporaries 1992*, 1992.
ACC99/1991

WILSON, Jane b. 1967 and **WILSON, Louise** b. 1967
8.30, 1992
c-type print mounted on plywood; 122 × 122; ed. 2/3; purchased from the artists, 1995. ACC12/1995

WILSON, Jane b. 1967 and **WILSON, Louise** b. 1967
Construction and Note, 1992
c-type print mounted on aluminium; 180 × 122; ed. 1/3; purchased from the artists, 1995. ACC15/1995

WILSON, Jane b. 1967 and **WILSON, Louise** b. 1967
Note, 1992
c-type print mounted on aluminium; 180 × 122; ed. 1/3; purchased from the artists, 1995. ACC14/1995

WILSON, Jane b. 1967 and **WILSON, Louise** b. 1967
Hypnotic Suggestion 505, 1993 (still)
back-projection video; running time: 55 minutes; 270 × 360; ed. 2/3; purchased from the artists, 1995. ACC13/1995

WILSON, Keith b. 1965
Untitled (Musical Instruments), 1995
mixed media; 10 parts, total 304.8 × 121.9 × 121.9;
purchased from the artist, 1997. ACC55/1997

WILSON, Richard b. 1953
Watertable, 1994 (detail)
vinyl and printed card; 18 × 18; unlimited edition; purchased from the artist,
1994. ACC48/1997

WILSON, Richard b. 1953
High Rise, 1989 (installation shot)
glass greenhouse, steel beams and 2 insectocutor units; 244 × 396 × 366;
gift of Charles Saatchi, 1999. ACC246/1998

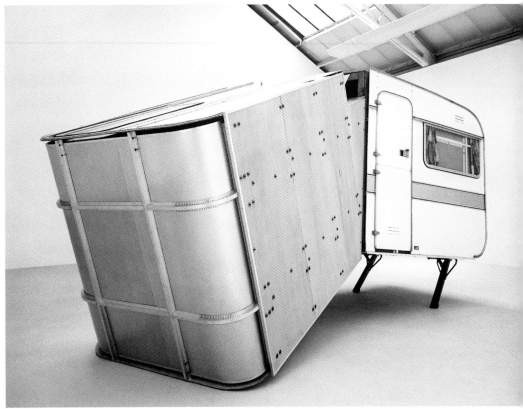

WILSON, Richard b. 1953
Facelift, 1991 (installation shot)
wood, steel, aluminium and cloth; 274 × 269 × 188; gift of Charles Saatchi,
2002. ACC50/2002

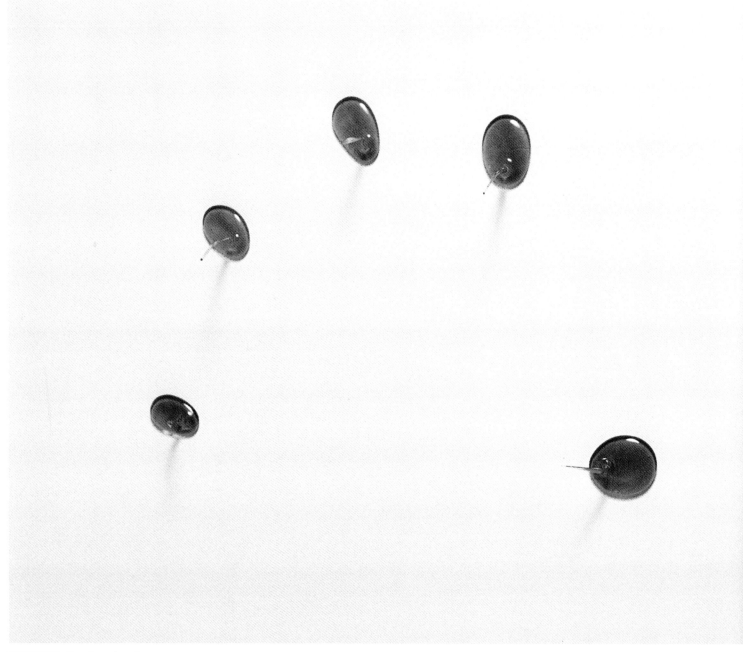

WILTSHIRE, Hermione b. 1963
My Touch, 1993
cibachrome photograph, glass, silicon glue and aluminium; 200 × 100 × 40;
purchased from Lisson Gallery, 1993. ACC1/1994

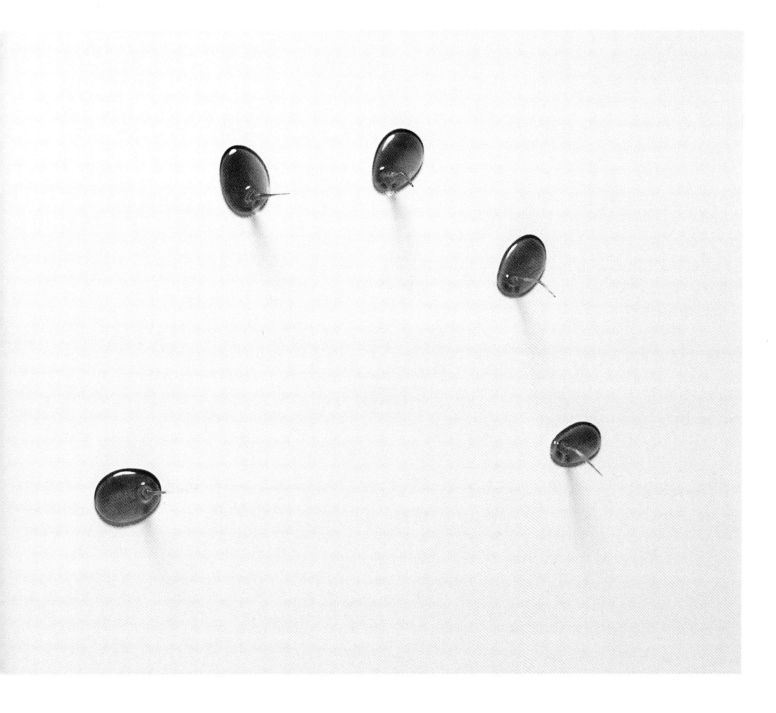

WINSTANLEY, Paul b. 1954
TV Room, 1991
oil on canvas; 160·1 × 170; purchased from Interim Art, 1991.
ACC67/1991

WOOD, Craig b. 1960
Untitled, 1990
plexiglass, PVC and water; 25 × 13 × 7; purchased from
Laure Genillard Gallery, 1994. ACC38/1997

WOOD, Craig
(see also LONDON portfolio)

WOOD, John b. 1969 and **HARRISON, Paul** b. 1966
Device, 1996 (still)
Betacam sp video tape; running time: 3 minutes; ed. 1/5; purchased from
the artists, 2001. ACC46/2000

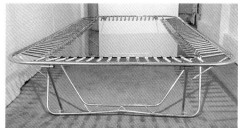

WOOD, Lucy b. 1969
Can't Play, Won't Play, 1996
glass and steel; 150 × 289·6 × 502·9; gift of Charles Saatchi, 1999.
ACC247/1998

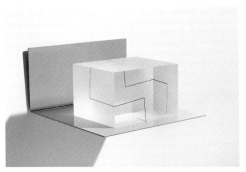

WOODLEY, Gary b. 1953
Study No.3, 1993
ink on acrylic perspex and cellulose painted aluminium; 8 × 12·5 × 10·5;
purchased from the artist, 1993. ACC15/1993

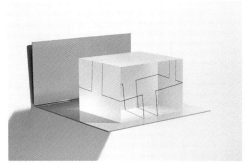

WOODLEY, Gary b. 1953
Study No.4, 1993
ink on acrylic perspex and cellulose painted aluminium; 8 × 12·5 × 10·5;
purchased from the artist, 1993. ACC16/1993

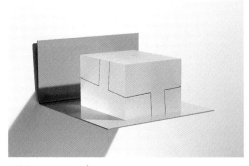

WOODLEY, Gary b. 1953
Study No.5, 1993
ink on acrylic perspex and cellulose painted aluminium; 8 × 12·5 × 10·5;
purchased from the artist, 1993. ACC17/1993

WOODROW, Bill b. 1948
93/29, 1993
oil stick on paper; 183 × 222; purchased from the artist, 1996.
ACC54/1995

WOODS, Richard b. 1966
Austin Metro (Red), Deptford, 1996
enamel on printed canvas; 245 × 366; gift of Charles Saatchi, 1999.
ACC248/1998

WOODS, Richard b. 1966
Peugeot 205 (Blue) Bermondsey, 1996
enamel on printed canvas; 243·8 × 365·7; gift of Charles Saatchi, 1999.
ACC251/1998

WOODS, Richard b. 1966
Volkswagen Golf (Green), Old Kent Road, 1996
enamel on printed canvas; 245 × 366; gift of Charles Saatchi, 1999.
ACC250/1998

WOODS, Richard b. 1966
BMW 525 as Biological Experiment (Green), 1996
enamel on printed canvas; 25·4 × 39·4; gift of Charles Saatchi, 1999.
ACC249/1998

WOODS, Richard b. 1966
Renovated Carpet No.1 (Burgundy), 1997
carpet, PVA and enamel paint; 330 × 122 × 1;
purchased from Hales Gallery, 1997. ACC8/1997

WRIGHT, Elizabeth b. 1964
Untitled: Newspapers and Tesco Bag, 1994 (installation shot)
paper and plastic; 2 × 70 × 60; purchased from the artist, 1995. ACC4/1995

WRIGHT, Elizabeth b. 1964
Pizza Delivery Moped Enlarged to 145% of Its Original Size, 1997
mixed media; 274·3 × 66 × 137·2; gift of Lux Gallery, 1999; commissioned by
London Electronic Arts to mark the launch of the Lux Centre. ACC24/1999

WYLIE, Rose b. 1934
Girl on Liner, 1996
oil on canvas; 183 × 163; purchased from the artist, 1998.
ACC71/1997

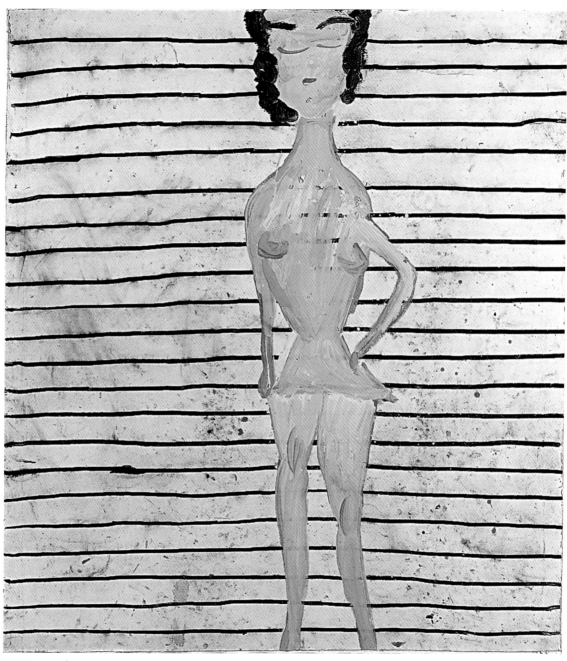

WYLIE, Rose b. 1934
Size 8: Orange, 1996
oil and charcoal on canvas; 183 × 165; purchased from the artist, 1998.
ACC70/1997

WYN EVANS, Cerith
(see SCREEN portfolio)

YASS, Catherine b. 1963
Portrait: Selection Committee for the Arts Council Collection,
1994
cibachrome transparency and light box; 2 parts, each 61 × 91·5 × 10;
purchased from Laure Genillard Gallery, 1994. ACC 27/1994

YASS, Catherine
(see also SCREEN portfolio)

Editors: Priscilla O'Connor, Sarah Reece, Anne Downes

Designer: Liz White

Layout: Compuscript

Illustrations: Compuscript, Denis M. Baker, Rory O'Neill

ISBN: 978-1–78090-075-9

1590

© Michael Keating, Derek Mulvany, Oliver Murphy, James O'Loughlin and Colin Townsend, 2012

Folens Publishers, Hibernian Industrial Estate, Greenhills Road, Tallaght, Dublin 24, Ireland

Acknowledgements

Worked solutions were provided by Jim McElroy and Denise Carroll.

The authors and publisher wish to thank the following for permission to reproduce photographs:
Alamy, Bridgeman, Corbis, Getty, iStockphoto, Science Photo Library, Thinkstock.

The following photographs were sourced from Wikimedia Commons:

Drassanes metro station, Barcelona (CC-BY 3.0; http://en.wikipedia.org/wiki/File:Drassanes_Tube_Station,_ Barcelona,_19th_April_2009.JPG); Tyson Gay by Eckhard Pecherk (CC-BY 2.5; http://commons.wikimedia. org/wiki/File:Osaka07_D6A_M200M_nearfinish.jpg); Men's 100m final at the Aviva 2010 UK Athletics Championships and European Trials, Birmingham, by William Warby (CC-BY 2.0; http://upload.wikimedia. org/wikipedia/commons/9/9a/Aviva_100m_Final_2010.jpg).

The authors and publisher wish to thank Bank of Ireland for permission to reproduce copyright material.